C

The world [illegible] Elves, Drag[illegible] and Wizards [illegible] series of ***Middle-earth Quest*** ™ **gamebooks**. You too can now become entwined in the world's richest tapestry of high fantasy.

Three Rings for the Elven-kings under the sky,
Seven for the Dwarf-lords in their halls of stone,
Nine for Mortal Men doomed to die,
One for the Dark Lord on his dark throne
In the Land of Mordor where the Shadows lie,
One Ring to rule them all, One Ring to find them,
One Ring to bring them all and in the darkness bind them
In the Land of Mordor where the Shadows lie.

Other *Middle-earth Quest* ™ gamebooks:

A Spy in Isengard™
Treason at Helms Deep™

Upcoming *Middle-earth Quest* ™ gamebooks:

Search for the Palantír™
Race from Rivendell™

Cover Design: Richard H. Britton
Content Editor: Peter C. Fenlon, Jr.
System Editor: Coleman Charlton
Production: Kurt Fischer, Jessica Ney, Paula Peters, Becky Pope, Eileen Smith, Suzanne Young, Coleman Charlton, Larry Brook, Leo LaDell

Standard (British) English spellings are used throughout this work.

Produced and distributed under an exclusive worldwide license by Iron Crown Enterprises, Inc., P.O. Box 1605, Charlottesville, VA 22902.

ISBN- 0-425-08993-2

Distributed by Berkley Sales & Marketing, a division of The Berkley Publishing Group, 200 Madison Avenue, New York, New York, 10016.

FIRST EDITION. PRINTED IN THE UNITED STATES OF AMERICA.

MINES OF MORIA™

by Susan Mathews &
J.D. Ruemmler

Editor : Kevin Barrett
Cover Art : Angus McBride
Maps : Rick Britton
Illustrations : Dan Carroll

INTRODUCTION

Based on the works of the greatest fantasy writer of all time, ***Middle-earth Quest***™ gamebooks invite the reader into the world of brave and cruel Men, Hobbits® and Elves, Orcs™ and Trolls™, and Wizards both good and evil. The continent of Middle-earth®, rich in adventure and conflict, provides the perfect background for solo adventures. Welcome to the fantasy and thrills of J.R.R. Tolkien's Middle-earth!

THE LOCATION MAPS

The two Location Maps preceding the prologue give an overview of part of the area in which your adventures take place. These maps show what **you** know about the area, but it does not tell you everything that may happen.

Each area on these maps is labeled with a letter and a number (i.e., A1, A2, ... , B1, B2, ... , etc.). Each of these labels refers to a section of the text, with the same letter and number, near the beginning of the book. This "*Location Text*" tells you what you find and directs you to further "*Encounter Text*" that gives you choices and detailed information to guide you in your adventures.

Keep track of your location on the Location Maps during play. This is done by remembering the label of your location or by tracing your path with a crayon or greasepencil.

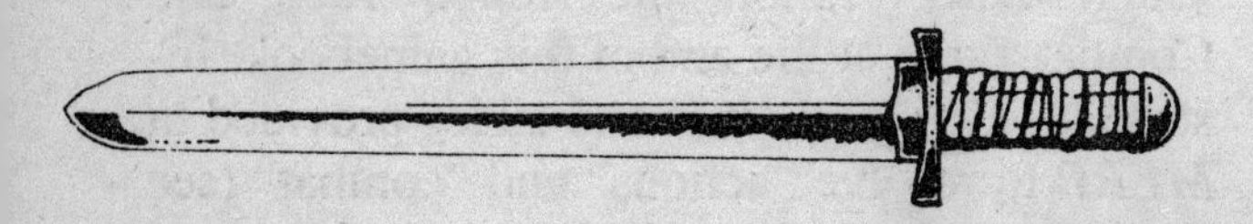

THE GAMEBOOK

The gamebook describes hazards, situations, and locations that may be encountered during your adventures. As you read the text, choices will be given as to what actions to take. The text section you read will depend on the directions in the text and whether the actions you attempt succeed or fail.

Location Text sections are in the beginning of the gamebook and are matched to the areas on the two Location Maps. These sections are labeled with a letter followed by a number. *Encounter Text* sections are found towards the back of the gamebook and are listed by three-digit numbers only (e.g., "365"). Read the Location Text only when you move into the matching area on the Location Maps, and read the Encounter Text when told to do so by the text.

CHOOSING A CHARACTER

There are three ways to choose a character:

1) You can use the *pre-created character* provided just before the prologue.
2) You can create your own character using the simple *Creating a Character* section at the end of this gamebook.
3) You can create your own character using ***MERP***, the ***Middle-earth Role Playing*** system (an ICE product not included in this gamebook). When using ***MERP***, ignore the Action Table and Combat Table at the end of this gamebook. Instead, use the guidelines and tables provided in ***MERP*** to resolve "actions" and "combat" (see *Optional Rules* at the end of this gamebook).

PICKING A NUMBER

Many times during your adventures you will need to ***pick a number*** (between 2 and 12). There are several ways to do this:

1) Turn to the Random Number Table at the end of this gamebook, use a pencil (or pen or similar object), close your eyes, and touch the Random Number Table with the pencil. The number touched is the ***number*** which you have ***picked***. If your pencil falls on a line, just repeat the process.
2) Flip to a random page in the book and look at the small boxed number in the inside, bottom corner of the page. This number is the ***number*** which you have ***picked***.
3) If you have two six-sided dice, roll them. The result is the ***number*** which you have ***picked***. (You can also roll one six-sided die twice and add the results.)

When you are instructed to ***pick a number*** *and add a "bonus"*, treat results of 12 or greater as "12" and treat results of 2 or less as "2".

STARTING TO PLAY

After choosing a character to play and a system to use, start your adventures by reading the *Prologue* found after the rules section. From this point on read sections as indicated by the text. When told to ***move on***, read text sections corresponding to spaces on the Location Maps.

THE BASIC *QUESTGAME*™ SYSTEM

TIME

When using the Basic System, **do not keep track of time**. When the text indicates a choice of encounters based upon time, read the text associated with the earliest time.

EQUIPMENT

Whenever you acquire money and equipment, record them on your Character Record in the spaces provided. Silver pieces are "money" and may be used during your adventures to pay for food, lodging, transport, bribes, etc. Certain equipment may affect your abilities. If you wish, refer to the Advanced System for the effects of armour and weapons.

"BONUSES"

When you are instructed to ***pick a number** and add a "bonus"*, the bonus that you should add is the appropriate "Total Bonus" in the "SKILL" section of your Character Record. Keep in mind that these "bonuses" can be negative as well as positive.

During play, you may acquire equipment or abilities that may affect your bonuses. The *Special Bonus* spaces may be used to record these bonuses; of course, some of the *Total Bonuses* will have to be recalculated if this occurs.

TAKING AN ACTION

When the text directs you to ***take an action***, refer to the *Action Table* at the end of this gamebook. Choose one of the actions listed and follow the directions given. Sometimes these directions will require you to ***pick a number*** and use the "Total Bonuses" listed on your Character Record.

FIGHTING

Fighting consists of a series of "rounds." During each "round," you attack your opponent *or* you attempt to flee **and** your opponent attacks you. Missile attacks and your Missile OB are **not** used in the Basic System.

After a fight, the text will indicate what you are to do next.

If you choose to fight an opponent **or** the text indicates that you must fight, the combat is resolved in the following fashion:

1) You attack (see below) your opponent and then he attacks you. This is one round of the fight (two attacks, two numbers picked). If you are surprised, reverse the order of the attacks for the entire combat.

2) Repeat step 1, one round of the fight, until one of the following conditions occur:

   a) One of you is **killed** (a "K" result on the Combat Table).

   b) One of you has more *Damage Taken* than *Endurance*. That combatant is **unconscious** and is defeated. (This can also occur due to a "U" result on the Combat Table.)

c) You successfully **disengage.** At the beginning of any round of combat, you may elect not to attack for that round. After your opponent makes his attack for that round, you may ***pick a number*** *and add your Running bonus:*

- If the result is 9 or greater, you successfully *Run Away.*
- Otherwise, you are still engaged and must begin another round of the fight at step 1. (However, you may attempt to *disengage* again).

How to Resolve an "Attack"

1) Subtract the defender's Defensive Bonus (DB) from the attacker's Melee Offensive Bonus (Melee OB) **and *pick a number*.**
2) Using the Combat Table at the end of this gamebook, cross-index the number picked (in the vertical column on the left side of the table) and the difference between the OB and the DB (in the horizontal row at the top of the table).
3) The result is the amount of damage that the defender takes (increase his *Damage Taken* by that amount). The special results "U" and "K" end the combat immediately with the defender being knocked out (U, Unconscious) or more rarely, killed (K).

Fighting More than One Opponent

If the text indicates that you must fight more than one opponent in a given situation, just "fight" them one at a time as indicated above.

DAMAGE AND HEALING

As you adventure, you will take damage from fights, traps, falls, etc. You must keep track of this damage in terms of a total amount of *Damage Taken*. (Record the total in the *Damage Taken* space on your Character Record.) Only your *Damage Taken* total changes during play; your *Endurance* does not change.

If your *Damage Taken* exceeds your *Endurance* (see your Character Record), you are unconscious. If this occurred during a fight, you are defeated and must proceed as the text indicates. Otherwise, your adventure is over and you may begin again from the start. If the text indicates that you "wake up", change your *Damage Taken* so that it equals your *Endurance*.

Each time you read a section of text that you have not read before and that does not require you to ***pick a number*** or fight or ***take an action***, you may "rest" and reduce your *Damage Taken* by one.

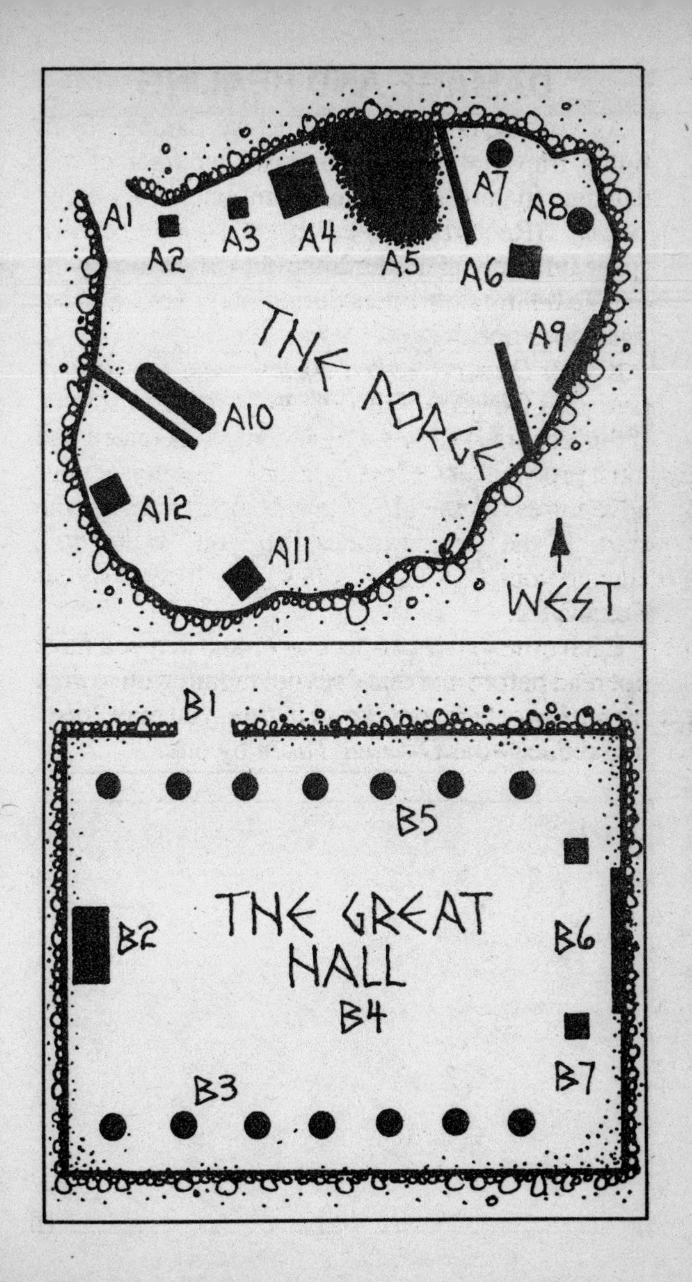

A1
A2
A3
A4
A5
A6
A7
A8
A9
THE FORGE
A10
A12
A11
WEST
B1
B5
THE GREAT HALL
B2
B6
B4
B7
B3

PRE-CREATED CHARACTER RECORD

NAME: TARLANG

DAMAGE TAKEN

STATS	Stat Value	Stat Bonus
Strength (St)	12	+2
Agility (Ag)	9	+1
Intelligence (In)	6	0

Endurance = 44 = 20 + (2 x St Stat)

SKILLS	Total Bonus	=	Skill Bonus	+	Stat Bonus		+	Special Bonuses
Melee OB	+3	=	+1	+	+2	St	+	
Missile OB	+2	=	+1	+	+1	Ag	+	
DB	+1	=	N/A	+	+1	Ag	+	
Running	+1	=	N/A	+	+1	Ag	+	
General	+2	=	+1	+	+1	Ag	+	
Trickery	+1	=	+1	+	0	In	+	
Perception	+1	=	+1	+	0	In	+	
Magical	+1	=	+1	+	0	In	+	

EQUIPMENT

NOTES:

CHARACTER BACKGROUND

(Read this if you are playing the Pre-created Character)

An adventurer and rogue, Tarlang was born five years before the War of the Ring, in a vale of Gondor's White Mountains. He grew up in Lamedon hearing tales of valour and victory and dreaming of Aragorn, Sauron, Gandalf and Saruman, and all the heroes and villains of the War of the Ring.

Now a brash, full-grown young man determined to discover adventure for himself, Tarlang has left his comfortable home in Calembel — high above the swirling Fords of Ciril — and has set out to make his fortune. (Fame also beckoned to him; Tarlang has long wished to be remembered in the songs of Bards, as are the Men and Wizards who fought and overcame the Dark Lord and his Nazgûl.)

The Fourth Age is still young. Tarlang is now a mercenary in the employ of Eomer, Rohan's King. He has been asked to banish roving bands of Orcs from the mountains overlooking Fangorn Forest. Journeying toward the mountains, Tarlang is distracted by the promise of even greater fortune. From a wandering friend named Elmarel, he learns of dangerous employment offered a trustworthy man by a family of Dwarves camped south of Lórien. Just south of the confluence of the Celebrant and Anduin Rivers, Tarlang comes upon a trading camp and a sizable group of Dwarves. It is here that he meets a very unhappy individual named Bror, and so begins this quest. ***Turn to the Prologue.***

PROLOGUE

Under the glimmer of brilliant starlight, camp-fires along the banks of the Silverlode promise warmth and companionship. A dark grove of pale-leafed mallorns stands like a wall to the north, on the far side of the river, forming one edge of the Golden Wood of Lórien. After traveling alone for weeks, you are drawn to the flames of one fire in particular. An acquaintance and fellow journeyman, Elmarel, told you some days ago of the gainful employ which may be acquired here.

You creep forward to the camp-fire, staying low. Peering out from behind a leafy shrub, you find a strange sight: two distinct parties of Dwarves, each composed of seven members, sit around a roaring fire. From the furtive glances they cast at one another, you gather that the two groups have reached an uneasy peace. What can they be doing? Elmarel gave you no idea that so many would be waiting here, nor did he mention that they would be Dwarves.

You begin to circle the camp, trying to get closer. Snippets of conversation reach you, but they are spoken in Khuzdul; the words mean nothing to you. Yet their tone has become excited and combative; you sense conflict between the Dwarves. Is this a ritual, or an onrushing brawl? Puzzled, you withdraw to a comfortable hiding place before you can be discovered.

Or have you? Your reverie is suddenly broken by a sharp exhalation behind you. There stands one of Durin's Folk, quietly glaring at you. Glancing back at the camp-fire, you note that one of the two groups numbers only six, obviously missing the fellow who faces you now, one hand on his knife.

"Have you been sent by someone?" asks the Dwarf in a suspicious tone.

"A friend, Elmarel. He said you might have need of a sword, and a good hand to wield it."

You watch as he sits on the trunk of a fallen tree beside you. "I am Bror, son of Bram, son of Bror," he asserts, introducing himself. The Dwarf glances about nervously, as if spies might be lurking close by. "Would you like to make a fortune as well as right a terrible wrong?"

Bror, son of Bram, son of Bror, is a typical Dwarf: short, stocky, and fierce-looking. He has dark brown hair and, when standing, is little over four feet tall. His beard is plaited and tucked into his belt. Bror wears a heavy cloak with a colourful red-and-brown hood, indicating clan and family.

'This sounds promising,' you think to yourself, recalling your empty purse and growling stomach. "Possibly. Go on," you say as the Dwarf's dark eyes glitter.

He continues: "For some time, my line of Old Bror's family has been deprived of our rightful inheritance by my dishonest cousins, who want not only their share of the family wealth, but ours too! They accompany me even now and watch me like Wights guarding a barrow. I have only a few minutes before they come looking for me. If you would help me, you must bring to light a Will which rests deep within Moria. A Will which can set aright the matter of our inheritance."

"Moria!" you restrain a desperate cry. "Moria is in ruins! And it must be thirty leagues or more from here."

Bror grabs your arm with impressive strength, then leans near to quiet you. "Take the path along the river west to the Mirrormere," he urges. "You must be quick! In fourteen days, the traders acting on our behalf will return from Lórien, and then we will be forced to leave this camp. You must return before then or you will never find us, and we will lose this slim chance of regaining what is rightfully ours.

"We have long known of this Will," he goes on, growing more serious, "but we — my kin and I — are unable to recover it. Our greedy cousins watch us too closely. It is our good fortune that Elmarel sent you to us."

"I am confused," you say, "about the origin of the Will."

Bror sighs, glancing toward the fire. "So little time! There were actually two Wills. It came about thus. Bram, my father and Old Bror's son, was a member of Balin's ill-fated expedition to Moria some years ago. They were trying to begin a new Dwarvish colony there, you see. In any case, Bram took with him one copy of Old Bror's Will. He hid that copy in our family's Great Hall in Moria." Bror points west, off towards the Misty Mountains. "If my father had become prosperous in Moria, I would have joined him there — but he did not. Instead, Bram was slain by Orcs. When this news reached us at Erebor, the original Will of my grandfather, Old Bror, was destroyed by our grasping cousins.

"Substituting their own version of the original Will, they have now taken away all that is rightfully ours! My brothers and sisters want their share of the family's lands and wealth. We must have the copy of the true Will hidden in Moria!"

"Indeed!" you comment. "And with your cousins watching, I suspect they would resort to violence if you or one of your brothers made ready to enter the Black Pit."

"Precisely. If I were to enter Moria for the true Will, my cousins would follow and stop at nothing to prevent its contents from coming to light." Bror hurriedly continues: "I have decided to send two agents, unlikely but capable, to find the Will in our Great Hall and bring it back. I would wish you then to escort my nephew, young Bain, into Moria. He knows how to find the Will. To you, I could not describe the intricate mechanism which I suspect guards it. I would send him alone, but he is very young and headstrong; the pair of you stand a better chance."

You begin to protest, but Bror raises his hand. "He is a dwarf. One of us — powerful, fierce and proud. You could find no better companion to see you through Moria. I insist!"

You wonder what commission you might ask. "Such a task might prove to be very dangerous," you tell him, taking a first step toward a favourable bargain.

"Very dangerous, yes!" he replies in a whisper. "For the Great Hall of my family is hidden deep within Khazad-dûm."

Khazad-dûm, Moria, The Black Pit — by any name, it is the greatest of all underground cities in Middle-earth, and rightfully a place of legend.

"It would be... interesting to see the halls of Moria," you admit. "But I have other interests which might suffer from any lack of attention." Although you have every intention of undertaking the task, you are determined to make the best possible exchange for your services.

Moments later, you reach an agreement and seal it with family oaths. You will search for and return with the Will; any treasure you find in the tunnels is yours to keep. However, you swear solemnly not to deface further the dwarf-mines of Moria.

"I have an old map of the secret tunnel my ancestors built to join our Great Hall with the heart of the dwarf-city. The entrance to this tunnel stands near Balin's more recent dwellings, but still far below the Chamber of Mazarbul. Of course, it has been many years since a member of our family of jewellers walked these passages, for the Balrog, Durin's Bane, long reigned in our ancient house. It is possible that passages have been delved since this map was drawn, but at least it shows the Great Hall — and that is where you must go! This key I give you now will open secret passages and chambers throughout our family's holdings."

4

The key which he hands you is a flat-faced iron plate with a small knob on the back; you immediately recognize it as a rune-key which can reveal the hidden tunnels Bror, son of Bram, speaks of.

"There are two or three other things which may be of aid to you," Bror continues, looking around nervously. "They are in this pouch which I will leave with you before I go. Remember: beware the many traps! Dwarvish as well as those Orc-made. And Orcs there are within Moria!"

Bror quickens his final instructions as you both hear the sounds of cracking branches and approaching footsteps. "Your complete lack of connection with my family is as important to the success of our plans as is your honesty," he tells you. "I do not wish to risk being seen with you. I will await your return at the appointed place and time: here, in fourteen days. To speed your journey, avoid Lórien and the Elves, who will not allow you entry into the Naith of the Golden Wood. Stay south of the river. The path will lead you to the Dimrill Dale, and on to the Dimrill Gate of Moria. I shall send along young Bain now; he knows the way. May good fortune go with you!" Bror disappears silently, a shadow in the mist.

The night is cool but pleasant. While you await the appearance of the young dwarf who is to be your companion for the next fortnight, you open the large leather pouch which Bror has left with you.

The pouch contains:

- A rather old but well-drawn parchment map *(see the map inside the back cover of this gamebook)*.
- A lockpick
- 3 doses of a healing herb (Mirenna) which reduces your Damage Taken by 10 and may be used at any time.

In addition to the equipment given to you by Bror, you may also have:

- 14 days worth of marching rations (waybread).
- A water skin.
- A suit of leather armour.
- A haversack.

In addition, you may take up to two (2) of the following items:

- A shield
- A shortsword
- A mace
- A bow with 12 arrows
- A quarterstaff
- A spear
- A ring which adds +1 to your Magical bonus while worn.

Enter all the items you wish to carry with you on your Character Record. ***Turn to 304.***

LOCATION TEXT: The Forge

See the Location Map for the Forge (precedes the Prologue). Read only the text for the Location you presently occupy.

A1 **Time: 0**

You have discovered one of the great forges of Moria's dwarves! From what you can see at the doorway, this was a Wire-works forge where Durin's Folk wrought the famous chain mail of Moria. Although not as well known as the armour, elegant filigree was also produced at the various Wire-works.

This chamber is a natural cave, but the rock formations have been highlighted by carvings and polishing. Light-stones set into the walls glow, bathing the chamber.

Note: When told to "Move on" inside The Forge, you may read the text for any Location beginning with an "A" (i.e., A1-A12). You may visit each "A" Location (other than A1) only once.

- *If you are finished at The Forge and want to leave,* ***turn to 130.***
- *Otherwise,* ***move on*** *to any "A" Location.*

A2 **Time: 5**

You discover a large stack of flat metal sheets used for forging bars, which would then be drawn into fine wire that the Master-smiths worked. Scores of these small sheets are neatly stacked, waiting to be put into furnaces — now cold. ***Move on*** *to any "A" Location.*

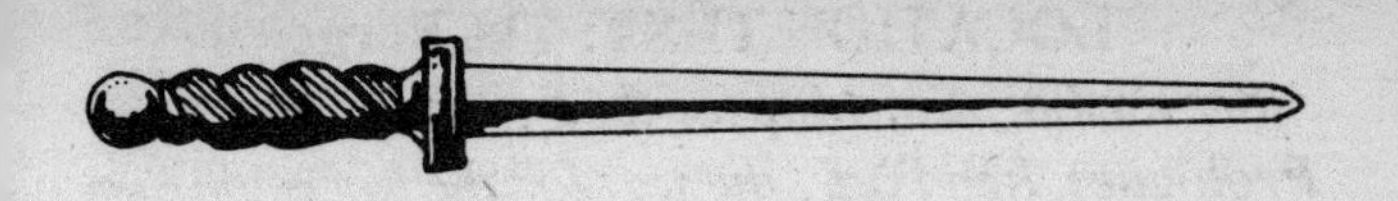

A3 **Time: 5**

Under a pallet of scraps and rags, you find a small stack of flat metal sheets waiting to be put into the now-cold furnace. These sheets are of various common metals. ***Pick a number*** *and add your Perception bonus:*

- *If 2-6,* ***move on*** *to any "A" Location.*
- *If 7-12,* ***turn to 200.***

A4 **Time: 5**

You come upon a large smelting furnace filled with rectangular baffles. The fire has long been extinguished in this forge, and the stone, once fired, is now ashen-cold to the touch. Within, several trays hold metal rods that were never removed, and long, thin wires that were never cut. ***Move on*** *to any "A" Location.*

A5 **Time: 5**

You find a large pile of anthracite coal, once fuel for the fires of the furnace. While walking around it, you stumble, dislodging pieces which spill in a small black avalanche around your companion's feet. A few lumps of coal bounce across the floor. ***Pick a number*** *and add your Perception bonus:*

- *If 2-6,* ***move on*** *to any "A" Location.*
- *If 7-12,* ***turn to 309.***

A6 **Time: 5**

You approach a workbench upon which rest numerous smithing tools, including hammers, tongs and a small anvil. A piece of chain mail, about one-foot square, lies beside a mound of metal pieces, each cut to the size required for one link. A curious device beside them seems to have been used to bend the metal into loops. The metal is a fine steel, though it now shows its age with rust and other corrosion. Bain points to a gash in the wood and a dried, blackened stain, which might have been blood, on the front edge of the bench. ***Pick a number*** *and add your Perception bonus:*

- *If 2-5,* ***turn to 204.***
- *If 6-9,* ***turn to 149.***
- *If 10-12,* ***turn to 331.***

A7 **Time: 5**

A circular stone pedestal rises from the floor. It is hollow, and the cavity at its centre reaches deep into the mountain. Careful examination reveals that a trap was set off, and whatever rested on the pedestal dropped into a deep pit. ***Move on*** *to any "A" Location.*

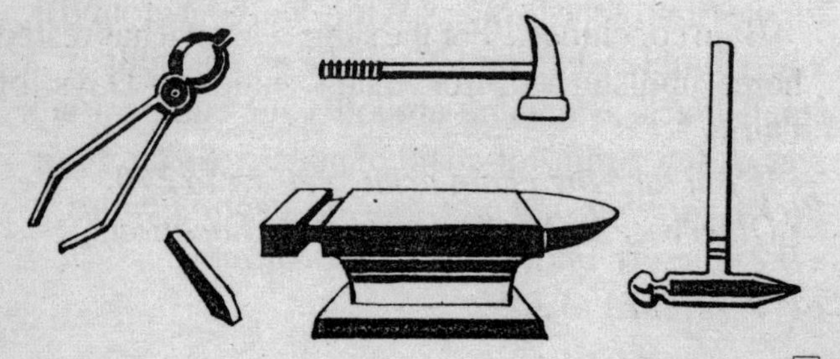

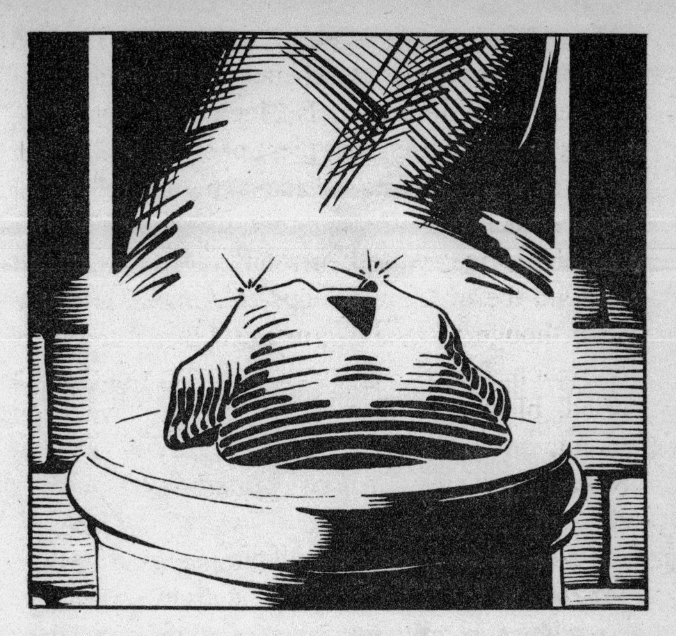

A8 **Time: 5**

A circular stone pedestal rises from the floor; displayed inside a glass case is a coat of fine chain-mail. Unfortunately, the chain coat is obviously sized to fit a a very small, young dwarf.

"My council is that we leave it," says Bain.

"Why?" you ask.

Bain concludes, "For the same reason it has rested here, undisturbed, for many hundred Days of Durin."

• *If you take the chain armour,* ***turn to 270.***

• *Otherwise,* ***move on*** *to any "A" Location.*

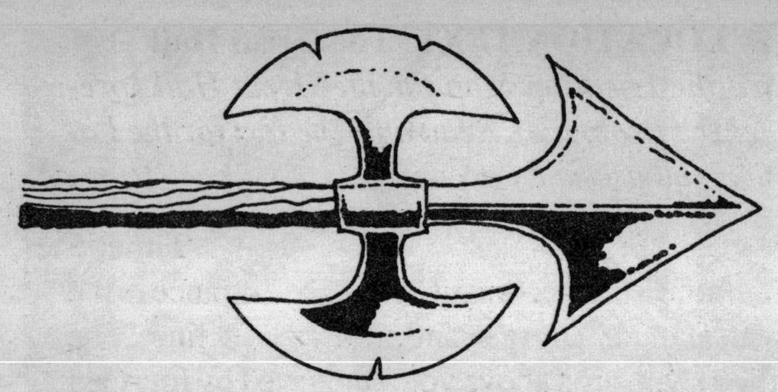

A9 **Time: 5**

Here, a huge cabinet made of carved wood stands against the cavern wall. Engraved runes can be seen on its side panels. ***Turn to 195.***

A10 **Time: 5**

You notice a large stone table once used as the focus of the chamber's foundry activities so long ago. A quick examination reveals nothing out of the ordinary, so both you and the dwarf continue with your search. ***Move on** to any "A" Location.*

A11 **Time: 5**

The piece of furniture that you walk toward is another well equipped workbench. The artisan who worked here must have specialized in jewelry and filigree, judging by the small tools left behind. ***Move on** to any "A" Location.*

A12 **Time: 5**

You approach a broad, wooden desk of drawers, with papers scattered about the top. The dust here is heavy and undisturbed. ***Turn to 384.***

LOCATION TEXT: The Great Hall

See the Location Map for the Great Hall (precedes the Prologue). Read only the text for the Location you presently occupy.

B1 **Time: 5**

You and the dwarf stand before the entrance to the Great Hall of Bram's and Old Bror's line. The ceiling soars high above you, supported by fourteen black marble columns. About midway through their height, tarnished silvery brackets support brilliant light-stones awakened by the presence of Bain's amulet. However, what they illuminate in the centre of the long chamber is a gruesome scene. On the floor lie the still corpses of three orcs.

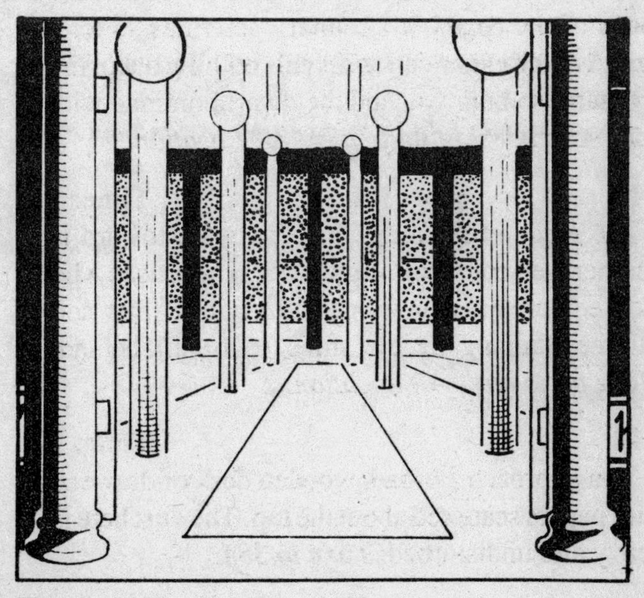

As for the rest of the chamber, the north end sports an intricate wall carving flanked by massive statue-columns, while at the southern end, nearest you, rests a low wooden table.

"My family's Will is close by. From this chamber, we must find the treasure-vault of Bram, but that may not be easily accomplished. Those goblin-bodies tell me that my uncle's cousins have preceded us."

"Or perhaps orcs of a rival tribe," you suggest, although Bain's explanation is far more likely. "In any event, if Bror's cousins or dwarves that they have sent in their stead are here, could they have reached the vault you speak of?"

"No," he answers, "They would need the rune-key, and only we have that."

"Then let us be on our guard, for they may still be waiting for us."

Note: when told to "move on" inside the Great Hall, you may read the text for any area beginning with a "B" (i.e., B2-B7), but you may NOT visit an area more than once. (Example: since you have already read the text for B1, you may not read it again.)

Consult the Location Map in this book. Then ***move on*** *to any "B" Location.*

B2 **Time: 5**

You approach a large wooden table seven feet long which rises to Bain's waist. A band of axe-head carvings run around the edge of the table, deeply carved by a strong, skillful hand. The dark hardwood has been polished to a sheen apparent through layers of dust. ***Move on** to any "B" Location.*

B3 **Time: 0**

You and Bain walk through a pair of columns on the eastern side of the Hall. ***Turn to 231.***

B4 **Time: 5**

Near the centre of the chamber you come to the corpses of three orcs, recently slain. Their black blood and twisted bodies partially obscure the intricate tile-work which decorates the Hall's floor here. The goblin's weapons are scattered and pose no threat, so you take a moment to survey the artistry of Bram's line. In the tiles, you can see many pictures formed: great dwarves in battle, mountains, vales and lakes, and stout workers carving deep tunnels.

"These form a story, if viewed in the proper order," says Bain, "though we do not have the leisure to discern it now. The orc-blood has taken its toll." ***Move on** to any "B" Location.*

You walk among the columns of the Hall's western side, where Bain, who is looking towards the wall, says, "There it is! The entrance to the treasure vault of Bram. We have found it!"

"We have found nothing," you retort. "It is a blank wall."

"To your eyes it is ordinary, but to mine, very special. See here?" Bain takes you over to the west wall and points out a slight irregularity in the stonework.

"What of it?"

"Bror gave you a special key, did he not? A rune-key." Bain is very excited.

"Yes," you answer, "I have it here." And you give it to him.

Your companion takes the flat surface of the device and presses it against the stone at chest-height. Nothing happens at first. But then cracks appear in the wall, though straight — not crooked as you might have thought. After a moment, a doorway appears fully-formed. "The elves of ages past called those of my race the Gonnhirrim — the Stone Lords. This, some say, is our most secret and skilled work. None could pass without knowing where the door lay, and that is the truth of Mahal."

- *If dwarves have been slain in the Great Hall,* ***turn to 413.***
- *Otherwise,* ***turn to 412.***

B6 **Time: 5**

The northern end of the Hall is dominated by two tall carvings of the heads of long-dead rulers, one set on each side of an ornate wall carving depicting the history of the Family and the Hall. The light is too poor for you to see much detail, but Bain finds the display impressive. ***Move on** to any "B" Location.*

B7 **Time: 5**

Bain leads you to a corner of the Great Hall. As you arrive, he says; "We are looking for an entrance to a secret chamber, and though that may sound easy — particularly if a dwarf is with you — finding it may be difficult."

To your left stand the high statues of the wall carvings dominating the northern end of the Hall. The figure to the right of the scenic display is a carved head of an imposing dwarf-king. The figure is hewn from rough granite and looks out over the Great Hall with a stirring pride.

"It is not here," says Bain. ***Move on** to any "B" Location.*

Read text passages only when directed to do so.

100 **Time: 5** **Exp Pt: 1**

As you grasp the pole and swing out over the shaft, all below you is unrelieved darkness. The pole is slippery, so although it is far to the bottom, you soon arrive. Bain follows shortly thereafter. Looking back up into the towering black, you realize that there is no returning that way. The small room at the bottom of the shaft opens into a wide corridor.

As you and Bain begin to walk along, swirling patterns of light-stones come to life in response to the amulet. There is no sound, nor betraying gust of air. Indeed, the weight of the mountain seems heavy above you in these lifeless corridors.

After a time, you come to a junction where a side corridor joins the main passageway. A hollow niche has been carved into the wall at the junction of the main tunnel and its offshoot. There, a basin containing clear spring water rests, and a stone bench is within easy reach. Ahead, down the main corridor, you see that the passage slopes down and becomes at least half-submerged in stagnant water. "Well, that does not look promising," says the dwarf.

- *If you enter the side corridor,* ***turn to 401.***
- *If you go down the main corridor and enter the water,* ***turn to 175.***

You climb for some time, surprised that this passageway is so straight when the other was so full of convolutions. In any event, this tunnel eventually leads out to a ledge overlooking a wide cleft. The ledge has obviously been hewn out of the surrounding rock, though the gorge beyond could not have been excavated by mortal hands. Once you gather your wits, you realize that this rift must cleave deep into the mountain and it is far to the other side. Every move, every breath echoes through the darkness and the sheer immensity of the gulf is staggering.

"What is this place?" you ask of the dwarf.

"I have heard stories," begins Bain, "of the vast caverns deep within the Dwarf-mansion, but this is beyond my imagining. This pathway here leads up. I would say we should follow it."

"I too. But you, Bain, should lead the way with that crystal of yours. In this darkness I would surely miss a break in the ledge, and judging from the fall away into the Deeps, that would be the end of my tale."

5

"Very well," Bain replies. The two of you make good progress in your ascent, for the ledge is sound and it climbs away into the distance. At times it changes into a shallow stair, and on occasion a minor gulf is bridged. Then there comes a narrowing where the sheer wall opposite comes within a stone's throw, and at this point another bridge spans the distance to an intervening pinnacle of rock, then onward to the other side. You cross over and continue on. All is quiet save the report of your footfalls which run away from you, then return from the top of the giant rift.

Eventually your path turns, delving back into the rock once more. You take a few tentative steps in, but the tunnel takes an abrupt dive down. "I do not wish to go down again," you tell the dwarf quite honestly.

"Nor I, but have we a choice?"

You return to the ledge and look about. When you look up, the answer comes to you. "There above us, Bain. I see a bridge at another level, and it is not too far." The dwarf inspects the wall of the rift beside you.

"We can climb it," he declares. "The wall is not as sheer as in other places, and it seems to me that hand-holds have been carved into the rock leading up that way."

7

You consider this. Although you believe that the hand-holds were probably carved out by orcs, they do lead up to where you want to go. “I am in the mood for another climb.”

“I will be right behind you,” says the dwarf.

The climb up the wall of the rift is not nearly so dangerous as you had suspected. When you reach the level of the bridge, and pull yourself up to the shelf which it opens onto, you are greeted by a most unlooked for and heartening sight. ***Move on** to B1 (The Great Hall).*

102 **Time: 10**

At first, this tunnel appears to be a dead end. A niche with a large statue of a dwarf-head carved in red stone stands at the end of the corridor, with what appears to be a rough, curved wall behind it. However, as you and Bain peer around the statue, you see a slender metal pole descending into a shaft in the floor. A pass between the levels of Moria! Such travel can be dangerous, for you will not be able to climb back up.

- *If you return to the previous intersection and take the left branch of the main passage,* ***turn to 274.***
- *If you return to the previous intersection and take the right branch of the main passage,* ***turn to 325.***
- *If you slide down the pole,* ***turn to 100.***

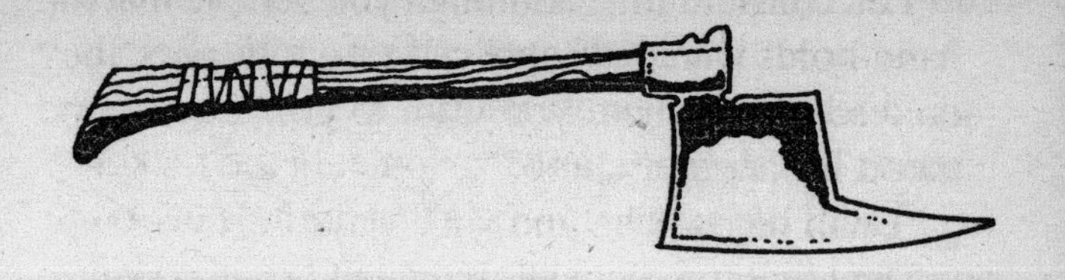

103 **Time: 0**

This junction forms the connection for three corridors. The arch over one passage is carved to look like a grapevine and has been set with purple light-stones. Another arch contains two niches, each holding shards of alabaster. The third tunnel is unremarkable, having no decorative arch.

- *If you go through the grapevine archway,* ***turn to 343.***
- *If you go through the arch with the alabaster shards,* ***turn to 375.***
- *If you enter the tunnel unadorned with an arch,* ***turn to 230.***

104 **Time: 10**

You walk through this section of tunnel and soon approach a meeting of corridors. ***Turn to 150.***

105 **Time: 0**

The troll-hammer catches you with a terrible impact, throwing you up against the cave wall. *Increase your Damage Taken by 30.*

- *If your Damage Taken now exceeds your Endurance,* ***turn to 146.***
- *Otherwise,* ***turn to 174.***

106 **Time: 0**

You do battle with the troll in front, while Bain is forced to defend against another coming up from behind. Tall they are, and fearsome. In the flickering light of the amulet, you see that the hide of your opponent is a pale, sickly green, but not like skin; the troll is covered with stony plates. You raise your weapon and charge.

- *If the melee weapon you will be using in this battle is magically enchanted with an OB bonus,* ***turn to 114.***
- *If the melee weapon you will be using in this battle is normal (i.e., without an enchanted OB bonus),* ***turn to 113.***

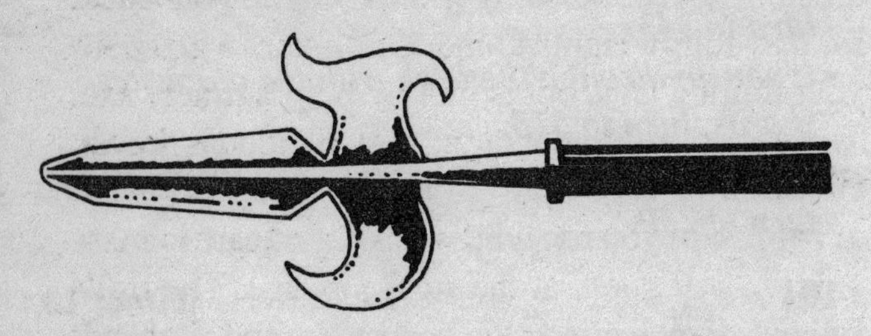

107 **Time: 10**

You step through the crack and stand inside a pitch black cave which the light-crystal has difficulty illuminating. Bain steps in behind you. "Why have you come this way?" he whispers.

"If we are being followed, they may pass us by if we hide here," you explain. You hear a quiet rustling from deep within the cave. "What was that?" you ask with half a trembling breath.

5

"Look back that way," says Bain. You peer into the inky blackness and spy a pair of eyes returning your gaze. Then another pair comes to life. Then four more! Red and flickering they are, swaying slightly and grouped together.

"Orcs..." Bain steps back. ***Pick a number*** *and subtract your DB:*

- *If 2-8,* ***turn to 399.***
- *If 9-12,* ***turn to 380.***

108 **Time: 10**

You scramble up a steep slope of stone to a wide crack in the cave's rock wall. Bain reaches the shelf first, and turning, helps you up. The laboured breathing of the pursuing trolls is hot on your back, for they follow right behind. One makes a grasp for your trailing legs, but is met by Bain's timely axe. There is a clang; and though no troll blood is drawn, enough time is bought.

The two of you run wildly, taking no care to mark your way or guess at the right passage. The trolls follow close behind, hurling stone and club but always just missing wide or high. The size and weight of these missiles are staggering. If you were hit, it would be the end; so great are they that no hero could withstand them.

Then, when you think that you have at last eluded the cave-trolls, there comes the scraping stone noise from all around. They have used other hidden tunnels to encircle you. Their battle-cries are now close by.

6

You and Bain stop for a moment to get your bearings and decide on the best escape route. Then Bain cries out, "Look there!"

"What?" you ask as you turn.

An answer is unnecessary, for a cave-troll stands only a short way down the tunnel in front of you. Dark and huge it is with a long stone hammer held by an arm so mighty it could mold the earth itself. The troll calls out and is answered by several others. ***Turn to 106.***

109 **Time: 10**

You scramble up a steep slope of stone to a wide crack in the rock. Bain reaches the shelf first, and turning, helps you up. The laboured breathing of the pursuing trolls is hot on your back, for they follow right behind. One makes a grasp for your trailing leg, but it is met by Bain's timely axe-swing. There is a clang; and you know that no troll blood was drawn, though time is bought.

The two of you run wildly, taking no care to mark your way or guess at the right passage. The trolls follow close behind, hurling stone and club but always just missing wide or high. The size and weight of these missiles are staggering. If you were hit, it would be the end; so great are they that no hero could withstand them.

At length, Bain is able to find a passage by chance which is low and narrow, by trollish standards anyway, though it seems a wide way to you. Your pursuers fall behind; their cruel curses come from a greater and greater distance.

"That is it," you gasp. "You have stole us away, and for that I am thankful." You grasp Bain's shoulder in gratitude.

"I too am happy," come the words of the dwarf. "And better still, ahead of us, I sense cleaner air and a better way."

"Then let us go there!" ***Turn to 184.***

110 **Time: 5**

The floor of this cavern slopes down toward a pool filled with quiet, black water.

"Your light, Bain. It is too dark in here for me." At your request, Bain holds up his crystal which reveals the deep shadows lining the walls.

"Back there," Bain points off to the left, "is an entrance to another tunnel, I think. Over to the right there is a deep crack in the wall. It is a fissure which may lead to another cave, but I cannot be sure."

As the two of you walk farther into the cavern, a dim but steady glow can now be seen coming from under the water's surface. ***Pick a number*** *and add your Perception bonus:*

- *If 2-7,* ***turn to 167.***
- *If 8-12,* ***turn to 170.***

111 **Time: N/A**

"Run!" you cry, but as you turn to do so, your foot catches in a shallow crevasse in the floor. Your ankle twists painfully, causing you to fall just as Bain — who carries the amulet — ducks into the side passage. Left in the dark, you try to scramble forward, but powerful and merciless hands grasp you from behind. The troll has you! You try to bring your weapon around, but it proves to be a useless gesture. You are knocked unconscious, and die shortly thereafter. Your quest comes to a sad conclusion. **The End.**

112 **Time: 10**

"Run!" you cry, then follow Bain — who carries the amulet — into the side tunnel.

Blindly flying down one tunnel, then another, you seem unable to lose your pursuers. At every turn you think will lead to safety, more trollish forms greet you with stone axes and hurled rocks. Near wit's end, you and the dwarf duck into yet another passage, but fortunately this one is somewhat smaller than the others, though you still think one of the cave-trolls could squeeze through. "This is good," says Bain. "We can move faster than they in here."

The tunnel becomes ever smaller, while the scraping pursuit of the trolls falls farther behind, until they can no longer be heard. ***Turn to 184.***

113 Time: 5

You strike at the troll's leg, but the blade is deflected without leaving a wound. The troll's skin is truly stone. Oh, what you would give for a ray of sunlight!

You must fight the troll, and in the following combat you may not Run Away. Also, you may not start the combat with a missile attack due to the confines of the tunnel.

(**TROLL** OB:6 DB:10 EP:50)

- *If you defeat the troll,* ***turn to 118.***
- *If the troll defeats you,* ***turn to 128.***

114 **Time: 5**

You strike at the troll's leg with your flashing blade, and although it does not bite deep, black blood comes from the wound.

You fight the troll, and in the following combat, you may not Run Away. Also, you may not start the combat with a missile attack due to the confines of the tunnel.

(**TROLL** OB:6 DB:6 EP:50)

- *If you defeat the troll,* ***turn to 118.***
- *If the troll defeats you,* ***turn to 128.***

115 **Time: N/A**

"Bain," you say just before the orcs come upon you, "we have no hope but to surrender ourselves."

You throw down your weapon and drop to your knees while the lead orc runs up to you, snarling and spitting froth. Bain is grabbed by many arms behind you, but the orcs have no mercy as the defenceless dwarf is cast over the precipice. Unfortunately, no better fate awaits you. Your quest has come to a sad conclusion. **The End.**

116 **Time: 30**

This trail is easy to follow, though disheartening, for the odour saps your strength and determination.

After a time, you come upon its source: a modest cavern with the centre a deep bowl and the outer edges rife with tunnel openings. "It seems all the paths end here," says Bain. "But what is this placc?"

The two of you step closer to the edge of the pit and see by the light of the amulet that it is filled with old corpses and refuse. The reek is overpowering. Your head swims, and for a brief moment, you feel as though your legs will come out from under you. It would be a cruel fall into the pit! ***Pick a number and add your Perception bonus:***

- *If 2-7,* ***turn to 402.***
- *If 8-12,* ***turn to 189.***

117 **Time: 5**

Checking the drawer carefully for traps, you find none. Opening it slowly, you discover a small brown leather bag bearing the design of a golden axe-head.

- *If you open the bag,* ***turn to 172.***
- *If you do not open the bag,* ***turn to 245.***

118 **Time: 0** **Exp Pt: 55**

You have defeated a cave-troll of Moria! But you have no time to take battle trophies. ***Pick a number:***

- *If 2-8,* ***turn to 369.***
- *If 9-12,* ***turn to 312.***

119 **Time: 0**

Clearly the bridge is safe to cross, so you and the dwarf proceed, wary not to look down into the depths of the chasm. Suddenly, as you reach the centre of the bridge, it begins to pitch and roll! The unexpected movement makes you lose your balance. ***Pick a number*** *and add your General bonus:*

- *If 2-6,* ***turn to 295.***
- *If 7-12,* ***turn to 317.***

120 **Time: 0**

This junction is the meeting place of four corridors. One corridor enters through an archway decorated with onyx-inlaid runes. Another passageway is partially blocked by a portcullis, which is half-lowered. Examining it, you see that it is firmly jammed. The third corridor shelters a broken carving of a dwarf- head; the head itself lies on the floor, while the shoulders and neck remain upright. The last corridor boasts a pattern of red light-stones. Perhaps they once spelled out a rune, but most are broken now.

- *If you go under the portcullis,* ***turn to 367.***
- *If you go past the red light-stones,* ***turn to 186.***
- *If you go through the onyx rune arch,* ***turn to 104.***
- *If you go past the broken dwarf-head,* ***turn to 171.***

121 **Time: 5**

The spring hall is a tall, circular, marble chamber with a vaulted ceiling and inset wall-gutters. Resembling a deep well, a reservoir stands in the centre of the room. Fed by a small streams flowing down the gutters like silver ribbons, the reservoir sparkles. The room is wet and cold, though very clean. Unfortunately, there is nothing of interest for you here.

"Let us get back to the main corridor," says Bain. "We are getting no closer to the Will here."

Turn to 328.

122 **Time: 20**

Here the passage slopes downward, taking you north. You check your map, but it does not indicate gradients. After traveling for some time, you come to an alcove set into the side of the tunnel. The disturbed stonework suggests an intricate pattern of diamond shapes. Within the alcove rests an overturned stone bench engraved with the scene of a forest full with leaves and blossoms. Beside the alcove lies a cracked basin shaped like cupped hands, but empty of water. The spring which emptied into it is now just a dry crack in the wall. Finished with your examination, Bain urges you on. "I am sure that we are in the main corridor indicated by the map. Let us hurry!"

Agreeing, you take the lead and continue doggedly on your quest for Bror's Great Hall.

Turn to 152.

123 **Time: 0**

"Well, truth be told there is but one sure way to find out about orcs in here. Follow me," you command.

"A moment first." The dwarf holds his ground.

"What is it?" You peer into the relatively small chamber trying to see if there are any places where orcs could be hiding.

“Look at this.” Bain stoops down and indicates oily black blood which has been spilled here. “It is orc blood, but not much. One of them was wounded here less than an hour ago I would say, judging by the freshness of it. There will be no orcs in there. They have been driven off, perhaps ahead of us. Their assailant left no sign, if only one there was.”

• *If you still want to explore the room,*
turn to 165.

• *If you continue to travel up the corridor,*
turn to 323.

124 **Time: 5** **Exp Pt: 10**

Good fortune is with you; the bats are driven off. As you prepare to leave the cave, your foot disturbs something on the cavern floor. At first you think that it must be the body of one of the smaller cave bats, but looking closer, you see a small cloth bag. Beside it lie a torn pack and broken sword. Apparently you and Bain were not the first visitors to this cave.

You open the sack and find a fine drawing of the Endless Stair, with markings for each opening from the stairs into Moria. Obviously sketched after the Wizard's battle with the Balrog, the rough map shows a missing section of stairs destroyed during the fight. With the dwarf trailing, you leave the cave and continue up the main corridor that you had been traveling before. *If you keep the Endless Stair Map, enter it on your Character Record.* **Turn to 122.**

11

125 **Time: 5**

"I cannot tell. Could those footfalls have come from dwarves?" you ask.

"No. They are orcs! And if my ears do not fail me, I think we are surrounded." Then in a loud and stern voice, Bain calls out: "You of the foul breed, stragglers left behind by Durin's Bane; hear me! You desecrate the halls of my forefathers! Come forth and meet your doom!" At this, Bain pulls out his amulet and holds it high into the heavy air. In the sudden gleaming, you see a large group of filthy, black orcs whom have stole up so very close to you. With hoots and howls and the gnashing of broken teeth they set upon you, scimitars raised.

"Put your back to mine and defend yourself!" cries Bain as the battle is joined.

Note that in the following combat, you may not Run Away.

(**ORC #1** OB:1 DB:1 EP:10)
(**ORC #2** OB:2 DB:2 EP:15)
(**ORC #3** OB:3 DB:1 EP:20)

- *If you defeat all three orcs,* ***turn to 137.***
- *If you are defeated by any of the orcs,* ***turn to 249.***

126 **Time: 10**

After crossing the bridge and walking for some time down a straight corridor, you and the dwarf come upon a point where the passage widens into a huge doorway. ***Move on*** *to A1 (The Forge).*

As you look around, a bat darts at you from the darkness above. A piercing cry proves that your attackers are scores of vicious bats, and they are large! "Vault Shrikes," says Bain who is already waving his axe. "Take a care that they do not bite!" With ill-considered aim, you make a frantic swing at the nearest, but they continually slip in and out of the shadows and are difficult to follow.

You must fight the swarm attacking you as a single foe.

(**CAVE BATS** OB:0 DB:5 EP:10)

- *If you defeat the bats,* ***turn to 124.***
- *If the bats defeat you,* ***turn to 159.***
- *If you successfully Run Away,* ***turn to 138.***

128 **Time: N/A**

The blow of the troll's hammer is your last sensation in Middle-earth. Defeated, your quest for Old Bror's Will has come to a sad conclusion. **The End.**

129 **Time: 5**

"Before we cross, let us be certain that no dwarvish or orcish stone-trap awaits," says Bain. Joining him, you carefully begin searching your end of the walkway. ***Pick a number*** *and add your Trickery bonus:*

- *If 2-6,* ***turn to 119.***
- *If 7-12,* ***turn to 355.***

130 **Time: 10**

You and Bain return to the bridge. Later, after forcing your way under the bent portcullis, you return to the familiar junction. ***Turn to 211.***

131 **Time: 0**

Here, three pathways intersect. The first displays a broken crystal vein originally sculpted to resemble leaves floating down from a tree in autumn, each decorated with tiny red, orange and yellow stones.

The second passage is entered through an archway with axe-head ornamented stonework. The chipped stones were fitted together so expertly that they require no mortar.

Inside the entrance to the third stands the shattered remains of a deep stone basin filled with clear, cold, spring water. "Do not drink of it," warns Bain. "While orcs remain in Moria, all is foul and putrid."

- *If you take the crystal arched corridor,* ***turn to 164.***
- *If you take the axe-head arched corridor,* ***turn to 294.***
- *If you take the stone basin corridor,* ***turn to 154.***

132 **Time: 5**

The orc seems to be intently observing something in front of him. He peers down a stairway at his feet, paying little attention to anything else. At the moment, his sword is sheathed, but you suspect that it would not take him long to draw it. Soon, he sits beside the passageway and leans against the wall.

Methodically, the goblin draws a knife and begins to sharpen it. This action does not comfort you, although you suspect that Bain is ready for a fight.

- *If you attack the orc,* ***turn to 207.***
- *If you motion for Bain to attack the orc,* ***turn to 236.***
- *If you continue to observe the orc,* ***turn to 361.***

133 **Time: 30** **Exp Pt: 5**

Lightning-quick reflexes save you and Bain! Hurling backwards, you barely avoid the collapsing ceiling.

Since the deadfall was designed to crush intruders rather than to block the tunnel, you see that the passage can be cleared. After shifting rocks and debris, you and the dwarf are able to squeeze past the boulders and into the hallway beyond. ***Pick a number*** *and add your General bonus:*

- *If 2-5,* ***turn to 136.***
- *If 6-12,* ***turn to 292.***

134 **Time: 15**

As you continue, the level of the water slowly drops as the corridor is on an incline. On the right, you notice that a small rock slide blocks a drainage basin.

Once the corridor is reduced to harbouring nothing more than isolated pools, you note a marked increase in mossy patches lining the walls. Also, large fungi grow out of damp cracks in the floor. The tunnel begins to dip again and curve, becoming more and more irregular. Finally, it splits again; this time it is not obvious which is the side tunnel. One branch veers left, while the other goes right.

- *If you go to the left,* ***turn to 327.***
- *If you go to the right,* ***turn to 352.***

Stunned and barely conscious, you finally awaken when you feel brutal orcish claws dragging you to the cave's wall, rusty manacles clamped onto your wrists. Unable to move, you cannot fight. Bain has been similarly bound by several more orcs who have recently arrived. However, the goblins have not yet taken your equipment. Two orcs turn from you to face another of their ilk coming from across the cavern. This goblin is larger than the others, and his clothing and armour are more elaborate (but no cleaner). He speaks harshly, seeming to be a commander. Unable to fully understand what the orcs are saying, you are certain that they are arguing. As their voices grow louder and their gestures more violent, you decide that the two in front of you are both claiming to be your captor. The argument intensifies; it seems that the bigger goblin is enjoying it, making no effort to stop them.

As your head clears, you remember your lock-pick. Moving slowly, you slip the small piece of metal into your palm and try to quietly move the chains so that the lock is within reach. The orcs continue to threaten each other; one places his hand on the hilt of his sword. ***Pick a number*** *and add your Trickery bonus:*

- *If 2-7,* ***turn to 282.***
- *If 8-12,* ***turn to 408.***

136 **Time: 0**

In clearing the passageway, you have strained your back. *Subtract 1 from your General bonus for the remainder of this adventure.* ***Turn to 292.***

137 **Time: 0** **Exp Pt: 60**

As you put down the third orc, his companions back away, then break into a wild flight toward the far end of the long cavern. You turn to find Bain wounded, but far from defeated. Four cloven orc-helms roll headless at his feet. "We must leave now, before they come back with greater strength," you say.

"On that we agree," replies Bain, "but which way shall we go?"

You and the dwarf return to the intersection where the main corridor branches right and left, and the small side passage stretches to an unknown end.

- *If you take the left branch of the main corridor,* ***turn to 274.***
- *If you take the unmarked side tunnel,* ***turn to 102.***

138 **Time: 0**

You race toward the entrance of the cave, nearly tripping over something you will never be back to discover! Once out of the cavern, you and the dwarf resolve to continue up the corridor in the direction you have been traveling. ***Turn to 122.***

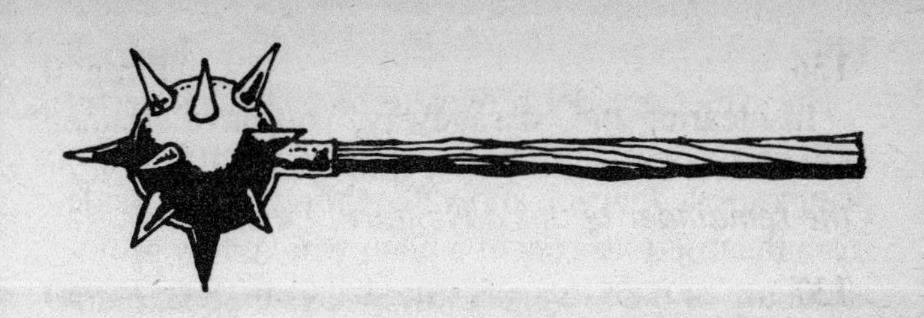

139 **Time: 6 Days**

Camping each night under the brilliant stars above Lórien, you and Bain find the return journey to be peaceful. Bain says little, but you suspect that he is just as fearful as you to greet Bror without bearing the Will. You follow the southern path along the Celebrant to the trading camp where the adventure began.

You find Bror pacing nervously at the eastern edge of his encampment. Before you have a chance to explain, he jumps you, beating you with his fists. "Fool! Liar! Weakling!" the enraged dwarf cries, spitting at you. At last, two fellow dwarves pull him away; you hope never to anger Bror again.

"Give me another chance!" you plead.

"I will kill you!" Bror threatens, restrained by his relatives.

Dejectedly, you slink into the shadows. Yet even in this dark hour, you sense the approach of adventure in the wind like an oncoming storm. "I will show you!" you cry defiantly, walking alone toward the river. **The End.**

8

140 **Time: 5**

The violet powder proves to be a very powerful herb mixture used in the treatment of burns. From prior knowledge, you know that the powder is made from the dried flowers of a plant which only grows at the top of the Silvertine. Bain says that the plant blooms once every year during the first full winter moon. *If you keep the Burn Powder, enter it on your Character Record. When your Damage Taken increases due to a heat-based attack, you may sprinkle all of the powder on the burn and remove that damage. This is the only way in which the powder may be used.* ***Turn to 195.***

141 **Time: 10**

As in so many other passages, you have no indication of where you are, or even if you now stand in an area shown on the map. You wish Bror, son of Bram, had not given you such an old and inaccurate rendering. Traveling in a northerly direction, you and Bain continue down the tunnel. ***Turn to 239.***

142 **Time: 0**

You and Bain quickly cross the bridge without further incident. ***Turn to 227.***

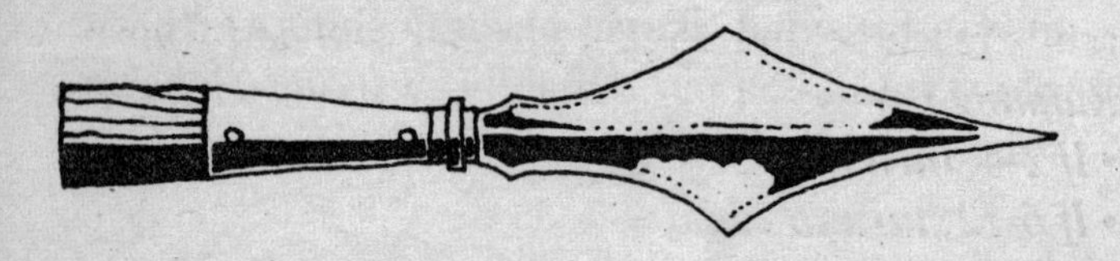

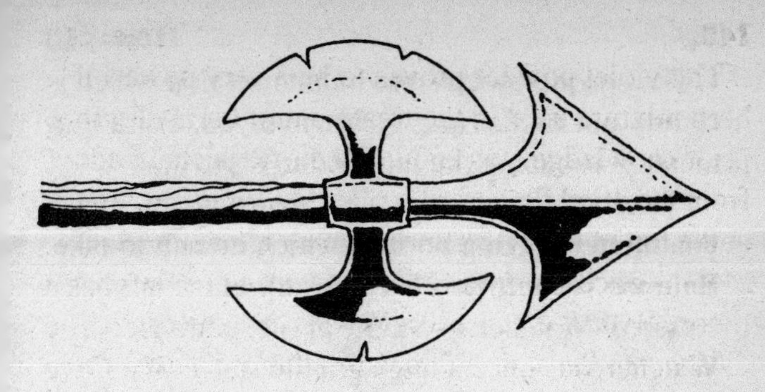

143 **Time: N/A**

Through persuasive speech, you finally manage to lure Bain to the bridge and cross the Celebrant to the south bank.

"We leave at sunrise." The rush of the river is a child's sleep-song, and you are soon dreaming of distant lands and strange peoples.

In the morning, you eat a light breakfast and set out for the Dimrill Dale with your now-quiet companion. ***Turn to 251.***

144 **Time: 0**

You recover from the surprise first and run for the tunnel leading to the stairs with Bain just a step behind you. You hear several orcs crashing into each other and growling as they follow, only an arm's reach behind. ***Pick a number*** *and add your Running bonus:*

- *If 2-5,* ***turn to 293.***
- *If 6-12,* ***turn to 256.***

145 **Time: 10**

The corridor opens into an intersection which is clearly not on the map Bror gave you. For a moment, you stare at the junction in disgust.

"I knew there would be a problem with this map," you mutter, having no idea which branch to take. Bain too is confused. The corridor to the left has a battered Watcher-in-Stone at its entrance. The Watcher was once a huge granite statue of a Cave Bear. Bain tells you that long ago the Watcher would have warned Moria's garrison of your presence.

The tunnel to the right passes under an archway decorated with bashed and sullied tiles displaying cracked yellow wild flowers against a deep blue background.

"Perhaps I should mark this on the map," you say to yourself before continuing. Bain nods in agreement though he continues to stare down the two separated tunnels.

- *If you take the Cave Bear passage,* ***turn to 318.***
- *If you take the flowered arch passage,* ***turn to 272.***

146 **Time: N/A**

Lost in a painful haze, your last vision is that of Bain running off as a dark troll come up and seizes your unresisting body. Your quest has come to a sad conclusion. **The End.**

147 **Time: 5**

There are several loose stones, some of which tumble into the water as you pass, but both you and Bain cross the bridge without incident.
Turn to 227.

148 **Time: N/A**

You are cruelly slain at the hands of a mighty Naugrim whipped into the frenzy of battle. Moria becomes your tomb as your quest comes to a sad conclusion on the verge of success. **The End.**

149 **Time: 5**

Looking closely at the workbench, you spy the outline of a secret drawer and manage to pry it open. Unfortunately the cunningly fashioned drawer is empty; the dwarf whose workbench this was must have spirited away the contents to a safer place some time ago. ***Move on*** *to any "A" Location.*

150 **Time: 5**

You and the dwarf recognize this junction as the first one you came to. The passageway branches into two well-constructed corridors; to the left, a crumbling Watcher-in-Stone in the shape of a large bear seems to guard that entrance. The passage to your right leads under an archway decorated with flowered tiles.

- *If you take the bear passage,* ***turn to 318.***
- *If you take the flower-decorated passage,* ***turn to 272.***

151 **Time: 0**

You have developed an irrational fear of Moria's caverns and passages. *Subtract 1 from your General bonus until you leave Moria.* ***Turn to 141.***

152 **Time: 10**

Unexpectedly, a room now opens off the corridor. The portal's arch is carved to resemble two trees; their uppermost branches meet out of arm's reach overhead. Tattered remnants of a leather curtain have fallen across the doorway. You cannot see inside.

- *If you enter the room,* ***turn to 350.***
- *If you continue up the corridor,* ***turn to 323.***

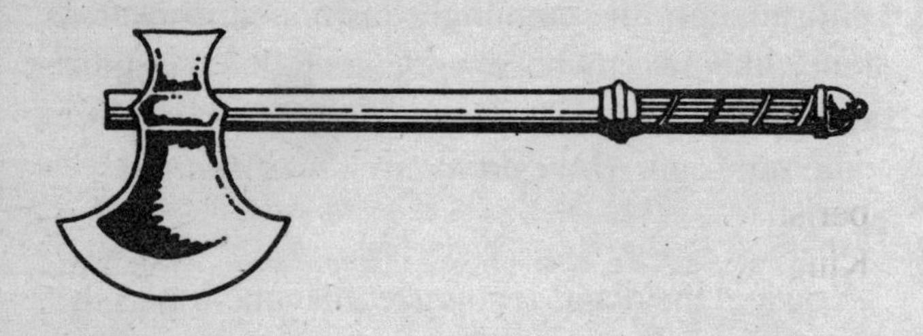

153 **Time: N/A**

With nothing to grab onto, you fall to your death deep within in the Mines of Moria. **The End.**

154 **Time: 20**

You travel another gloomy corridor for some distance with only Bain's pale amulet to light your way. Finally, you come to an archway upon which is a green crystal rune. Beyond is another meeting of passageways. ***Turn to 210.***

Passing under a high arch, Bain trails you down this wide corridor. Shortly, you approach a low door to the left standing partly open. The dwarf motions for you to enter. Within the narrow corridor you turn right and reach the bottom of a flight of stairs and begin to ascend.

"Bain?"

"Yes, what is it?" comes his voice, whispering.

"With the Balrog of Moria slain, and Mordor's Dark Lord cast down, his hosts scattered — why have the Dwarves of Durin's line not come to reclaim these halls?"

"We have suffered grievous losses in wars now past," explains your companion. "Dain Ironfoot was lost with many warriors while defending Erebor against an Easterling assault. Before him, Thorin Oakenshield and the better part of our tribe perished at the Battle of Five Armies. Our new King, Thorin Stonehelm, deems that the time is not yet ripe for our ascendance. But we will have our due, when our numbers are stronger. Once restored, the Dwarf-mansion will never again be abandoned. Durin the Lastking will sit on Moria's throne!"

You and Bain have now climbed a flight of fifty or more stairs. From Bror's instructions you discern that the passage to his family halls should be nearby. Bain passes you with his light-crystal before him. "Here it is," he says stiffly "but this indeed bodes ill for us."

10

"What is the matter?" you ask, though as you approach in the darkness you can see for yourself. The door which leads into the tunnels and chambers of Bror's family, a door that was to have been concealed and secret, stands ajar. "Others came before us," you say.

"Aye, that is the truth of it," says Bain. "And whether they be orcs, or dwarves of our rival band, I cannot guess."

- *If you continue up the secret passage to the Chamber of Records,* **turn to 347.**
- *If you pass through the door leading to Bror's family halls,* **turn to 198.**

156 **Time: 0**

You haul back the lid of the heavy trunk and peer inside. There, laying on top of the container's other riches, you find a fine, grey cloak just long enough to fit you. This you snatch up and arrange across your shoulders.

Note that the cloak, when worn, will increase your DB by 1. Add the cloak to your Character Record if you wish to play this character in another Middle-earth Quest book. **Turn to 301.**

3

157 **Time: 5**

"We fight or die!" you call back to Bain above the sound of the drums.

"Aye!" he says. "Good fortune to us!"

Bain swings his axe at the first orc which rushes up the stairway to his feet, and sends the goblin's head back into the host of others. Inspired, you turn to meet your foes with keen steel.

You must fight these orcs of Khazad-dûm, and may not Run Away.

(**ORC #1**	OB:3	DB:2	EP:20)
(**ORC #2**	OB:2	DB:0	EP:10)
(**ORC #3**	OB:1	DB:3	EP:12)
(**ORC #4**	OB:5	DB:2	EP:22)

- *If you defeat the four orcs,* ***turn to 406.***
- *If any orc defeats you,* ***turn to 405.***

158 **Time: 20**

You awake and see the face of Bain above yours. "I am pleased to see you alive, my friend."

"I too," you say, though that is painful. "What of the other dwarves?"

"They were two of my uncle's cousins, as we had thought, but they can trouble us no more." To one side, their bodies are heaped together on the floor.

"Your work?" you ask.

"Do you see another?" Bain is proud to have secured this threat, but there is still the Will to find. He helps you to your feet. *Reduce your Damage Taken to equal your Endurance.* ***Move on*** *to any "B" location.*

159 **Time: 0**

The bats are too many and too fierce! You are overcome by them. ***Pick a number:***

- *If 2-9, **turn to 372.***
- *If 10-12, **turn to 329.***

160 **Time: 0**

Both you and Bain manage to get past the orc and take flight down the stairs he seemed to be guarding. You leave the orc behind, but one of you accidentally activates a trap on the stair. With a loud "snap!" a gaping pit opens at your feet. Desperation lends you strength, and you make a mighty leap. ***Pick a number** and add your General bonus:*

- *If 2-6, **turn to 357.***
- *If 7-12, **turn to 308.***

161 **Time: N/A**

"I know we will be late, but may good fortune smile upon us!" you say to Bain. ***Turn to 348.***

162 **Time: 5**

As you continue, the passage has sloped down enough to bring the water up to your waist. Bain spies a low corridor off to the right diverging from the main tunnel. When you come to it, you discover that this side tunnel becomes completely submerged after a short way. "We might try it anyway," you suggest. "Perhaps it rises up after a few yards."

"I think not," counters Bain. "That way is probably blocked with water as far as we could go.

- *If you continue along the main corridor,* ***turn to 134.***
- *If you try the side corridor despite Bain's warning,* ***turn to 340.***

163 **Time: 0**

The urn has a wax stopper clogging its mouth, Once you clear that away, you find that it is full of a pungent wine. The cordial, you would guess, is fine indeed and would fetch a great price in the right market, but the urn is far too heavy for you too carry alone, or with Bain's help if he would offer it. You turn away from the container. ***Turn to 301.***

164 **Time: 15**

You and the dwarf walk on through the semi-darkness. Finally, you come to an archway carved so as to look like a large grapevine ripe with fruit. ***Turn to 103.***

165 **Time: N/A**

"Maybe the foul creatures left something behind. Bring your light in here and we will have our look." You then advance into the wretched chamber.

"Tread carefully," warns the dwarf.

Turning back to scorn his overly-cautious ways, your stride brings you over one of the orc-mats, and it gives way beneath your feet! You fall down a deep shaft, and do not live to again see your companion, Bain. **The End.**

166 **Time: 15**

Diligent application of your lockpicking skills, spurred on by a few directions from Bain produce no results. You are unable to open the chest and give up in disgust. Leaving the room, you soon arrive back at the corridor junction. ***Turn to 120.***

167 **Time: 0**

You ask Bain a question. "That illumination from the pool—could it be light-stones coming to life for your amulet?"

"Perhaps," says the dwarf. "The light does grow stronger as we approach."

- *If you return to the last intersection and continue down the main corridor,* ***turn to 175.***
- *If you explore the tunnel to the left,* ***turn to 244.***
- *If you examine the still pool more closely,* ***turn to 281.***
- *If you explore the fissure to the right,* ***turn to 316.***

168 **Time: 5**

The papers on the top of the desk are designs for a gold necklace having twenty-eight tiles linked together by a fine chain. It seems that each plate was to be engraved with a different scene from Moria's history. Bain is clearly intrigued by the sketches and insists that he takes them. Without an objection from you, he does so. ***Turn to 384.***

169 **Time: 6 days Exp Pt: 50**

You and Bain are propelled down the flume at great speed; your dark, dizzying journey ends with a 'whoosh!' and a dramatic fall into a calm body of water. You bob serenely for a few moments while regaining your senses. But is it the Mirrormere? The Celebrant? Or some unknown stream?

Bain calmly opens the barrel's top and peers out. "We are in the Silverlode, below Kheled-zâram," he whispers, eyes wide with wonder.

As you crouch in the barrel, Bain paddles to shore. After he climbs out, you follow. The clean air and bird-song tell you that your mission has almost reached its conclusion. After pausing to eat and drink beneath the towering peaks called Redhorn and Cloudyhead, you and the dwarf begin walking east toward the Anduin, to meet Bror, son of Bram, and hand over the Will. The trek is slower now, for you carry booty and are weary from fighting and fleeing orcs, but progress is steady.

Sleeping each night under the brilliant stars above Lórien, your journey is peaceful. Bain says little, but you suspect that he is just as excited to have have been in the Black Pit — and survived. You follow the southern path along the Celebrant to the trading camp where you first met the dwarves and the adventure began. ***Turn to 362.***

170 **Time: 0**

You ask Bain a question. "That illumination from the pool—could it be light-stones coming to life for your amulet?"

"Perhaps," says the dwarf. "The light does..."

You interrupt Bain. "What was that?" You have just seen a few small bubbles break the surface of the pool. As their ripples come out to the rock at the edge, Bain stops walking for a moment and lifts his crystal a little higher, as if its rays might pierce the water and reveal what lies underneath.

"I know not," answers Bain, "nor may we want to."

- *If you return to the last intersection and continue down the main corridor,* ***turn to 175.***
- *If you explore the tunnel to the left,* ***turn to 244.***
- *If you examine the pool more closely,* ***turn to 281.***
- *If you explore the fissure to the right,* ***turn to 316.***

171 **Time: 5**

This corridor containing a stone dwarf-head ends at a door. The door is crafted of a polished white wood inlaid with onyx stone, but the portal is charred, as if once exposed to a great heat. "Durin's Bane," you hear the dwarf whisper.

- *If you enter through the door,* ***turn to 345.***
- *If you go back to the last junction,* ***turn to 120.***

172 **Time: 5**

The bag is filled with a very fine powder the colour of forest violets. ***Pick a number*** *and add your Perception bonus:*

- *If 2-7,* ***turn to 252.***
- *If 8-12,* ***turn to 140.***

173 **Time: 5**

As you try to disarm the trap, you hear the scraping of metal grinding on stone. You and the crest-fallen dwarf can only stand and watch as the base of the container opens and the marvellous coat of mithril mail falls down a deep shaft into some unknown Deep of Moria.

"Fool!" cries Bain. "Do have any idea how much that was worth to my kinsmen? A fortune! I do not exaggerate. And you lost it! I would not tell Bror of this if you would like to keep your head." His words are fell, but they ring true. It is unfortunate that you could not have recovered the coat. ***Move on*** *to any "A" Location.*

174 **Time: N/A**

Though the hammer has not killed you, the impact of it causes you to fall to the ledge. "Bain..." you wheeze, "help me..."

Although the dwarf tries to help you back up, he is cast aside by a troll who has quickly come up from behind. Then, as the beast grabs you, your world goes black, and you know no more. Your quest has come to a sad conclusion. **The End.**

175 **Time: 10**

Soon you begin splashing through this watery tunnel, though the liquid is fetid and foul.

Turn to 162.

176 **Time: 120** **Exp Pt: 30**

"Good work," says your companion. "There will be plenty more of that for my people in this new Age."

Searching the fallen goblins reveals nothing of value, as you suspected. A few moments later, Bain easily convinces you that it would be best to return to the passage leading to the Chamber of Records.

Retracing your steps as best you can, you find the passage and within, ascend a great flight of stairs.

Turn to 155.

177 **Time: 5**

"Friend, Bain. I believe that in entering Moria you have taken leave of your senses. Who ever heard of water rebelling against anything? I will drink." And with that you once again bend down, but this time take a long drink of the cool water.

At first it seems wholesome. You are about to rebuke Bain one more time when your vision suddenly darkens and your head spins. When you open your eyes, for indeed they shut of their own accord, you realize that you are lying on the floor of the passageway, the dwarf hovering over you. There is a grave sickness in you, and you wish for nothing more than to be ill. But that does not come. Bain helps you back to your feet without a word, though his face is sternly set.

"I am fine," you lie. "I can walk without your help." With that you stumble under the archway into the next intersection of tunnels. *Due to the effects of the spring water, reduce all of the Total Bonuses listed on your Character Record by 1 each for the remainder of the adventure.* **Turn to 131.**

178 **Time: N/A**

You and Bain continue moving down the tunnel, hoping that the tunnel will rise above the water level and give you a chance to breathe. Finally, you realize that you have gone too far; you have no choice except to keep going forward. At last, and sadly, the bone-chilling water overcomes you and the dwarf. Your quest is over. **The End**

You and Bain stand in a narrow passage leading into a large, natural cave which lies to the south-east; it is wide with a ceiling that looms far above. There is also a faint but constant glow that your eyes slowly adjust to. It is not the light of the sun filtering down through deep cloven shafts, so you wonder at it, particularly the yellow colour. A feeling of great, heavy space overtakes you as you move to the centre of the cave. Looking over your shoulder, expecting to find some huge cave- creature poised to attack, you meet only the intense gaze of the dwarf. He is a dim figure in the unearthly radiance, but ready to meet any challenge, and that is good!

The floor of the cave is smooth and the dust has been disturbed before you. Looking about, you realize that the light emanates from strange mosses growing on the cavern's walls. There is an odour in the air now, something unwholesome, but you do not recognize it.

Then you notice a rift of blackness to the south-east. From your map, you would guess that this would be the entrance to the passageway you seek. You motion, and Bain stays close behind.

Turn to 409.

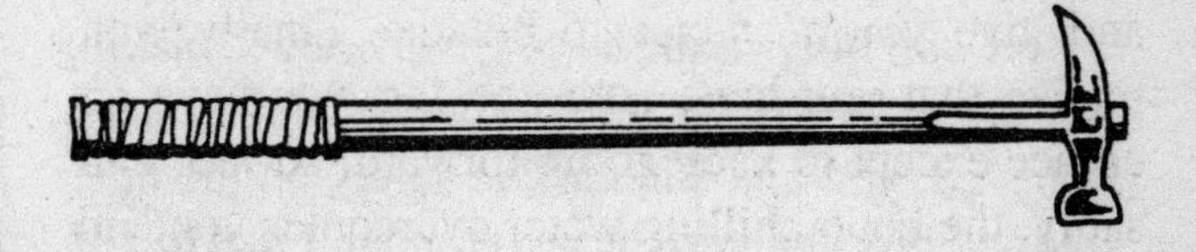

180 **Time: 20**

Although you become confused at certain points, you manage to find a way out to the cave with the pool. From there you pass out and return to the main passage. Ahead in the gloom you see the tunnel which dips down into a liquid mire.

"Little better, but this will be a safer way, I think." Bain's words lend you strength, and the two of you proceed. ***Turn to 175.***

181 **Time: 20**

Although you become confused at certain points, you manage to find a way back out to the cave. It is but a few short steps to the edge of the pool. ***Turn to 281.***

182 **Time: N/A**

You have lingered too long in Lórien! From the woods, three tall elves with longbows drawn taught appear like silent spirits. You must flee! Grabbing Bain, you race toward the bridge and the river Celebrant. ***Pick a number*** *and add your Running bonus:*

- *If 2-11,* ***turn to 262.***
- *If 12,* ***turn to 248.***

183 **Time: 10**

You carefully walk across the bridge, making sure not to look down into the depths of the chasm. Relieved, you and Bain arrive safely on the other side and proceed into the next tunnel. ***Turn to 141.***

184 **Time: 5**

The two of you rest for a moment, then pass out of the troll-tunnels into more familiar environs. To your left comes the soft glow of dwarvish light-stones which show a corridor junction. You thought you would never be so happy to see one of those again!

"I have my bearings again," says the dwarf. "This corridor heads to the north and east. You may lead again if you wish."

Thanking the dwarf, and so very glad to be out of the troll-hole, you move out in front with purpose, coming to the intersection. ***Turn to 211.***

185 **Time: 20**

Although you become confused at certain points, you manage to find a way back to the cave. Once there, you give the pool a wide berth and cross to the rock fissure. ***Turn to 316.***

186 **Time: 15**

Your footsteps echo eerily as you walk down the stone hallway. Dust and grit rest heavily on the floor. The tunnel twists and turns its way underground, but seems to remain fairly level. You walk under another archway, this one decorated by an exposed vein of golden ore running through the rock. The archway leads to another corridor junction obviously not marked on your map.

Turn to 210.

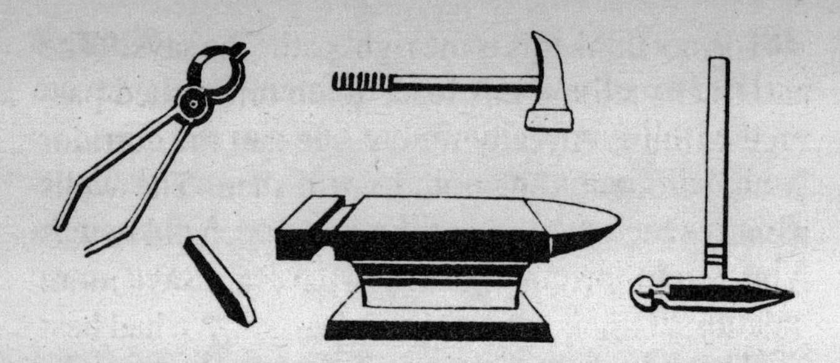

187 **Time: 30**

Both you and the dwarf travel for some distance through this gently curving tunnel. There are no light-stones set in the walls, so Bain's amulet provides the precious little light available to you. The cart tracks follow along on the left, and no fissure or portal breaks the wall of the passage. "New construction," says Bain. When he talks, his words boom in your ears, for all has been silent for so long.

"Quietly, Bain," you insist, "would you have me catch my death of fright, or warn more orcs of our presence here?"

"To answer your second question, there has been no light here for hundreds of years. For those used to living in this accursed darkness, my little crystal must be like the sun suddenly stabbing into the deepest hole of Barad-dûr. Any would know we were here long before they could hear us. As for your first question, I have no comment, other than it would be more worth while dying while killing those terrible orcs." Bain then is quiet for a Time before he speaks again.

5

"I do not think this is the right path," he says. "The cart tracks tell me this leads to an unfinished passage or mine. Already we can see that the corridor is more roughly hewn and unfinished. The walls have not been braced, or the wood which did so was long carried off and burnt." Then Bain says more gravely; "I think this ceiling is unsafe; We had best return the way we came."

You look around in the shadowy tunnel and decide that Bain speaks truly. The only finished portion of the corridor is the floor, which though flat, has begun a shallow decline, descending deeper into Moria's brooding rock. Then, just ahead you spy a broad shape forming in the pale light. "What is that?" you ask.

"My eyes tell me it is a cart which once would have used the tracks here," answers Bain.

- *If you approach the cart, **turn to 390.***
- *If you return to the last junction, **turn to 351.***

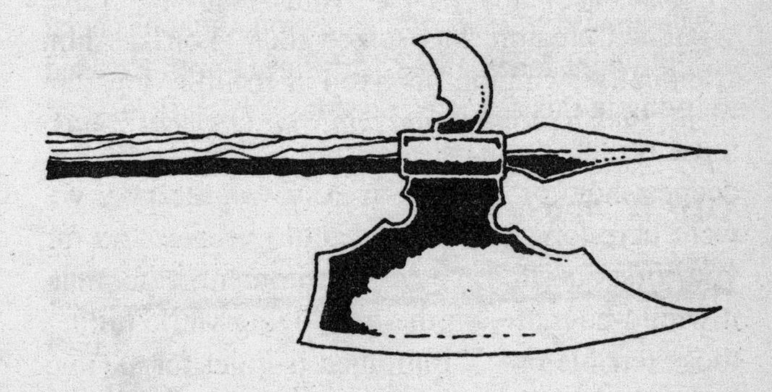

"I will go, but here — give me the crystal first. I must see where I would go." Reluctantly, Bain gives you the amulet on its heavy chain. This you cast about your head, leaving the crystal atop your tunic, then hoist yourself up into the base of the fissure. The pale radiance of the amulet reveals a steeply upward-sloping crack which you follow as best you can, disregarding the sharp rock and sliding gravel.

"This is a cursed way," you say back to your companion, who seems to be having a better time of things. Just ahead, you see that the way becomes much too narrow for either of you to pass. "We can go no further," you call down. Bain is about to answer you when he gives a short wail, then slides back down out of the fissure. Has he slipped and fallen? No! You see that something gruesome has grabbed his leg. "Bain!" you call out.

"Quickly!" he gasps from below, "Some wretched creature has seized me." You see him frantically swinging his axe but to little apparent avail. ***Pick a number** and add your General bonus:*

• *If 2-7, **turn to 381.***
• *If 8-12, **turn to 218.***

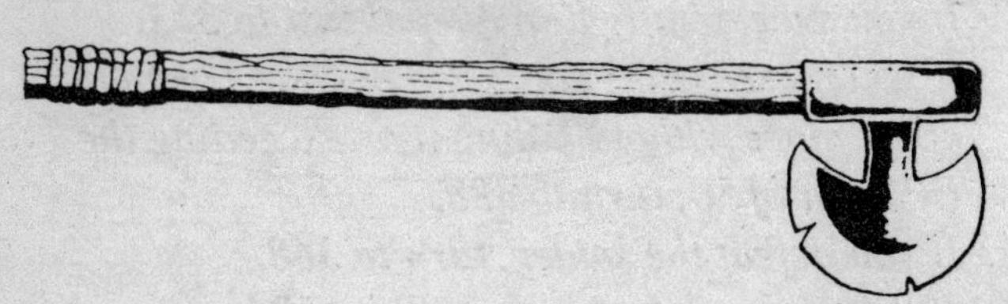

189 **Time: 5**

"Bain!" you cry out in a hoarse voice. "Look behind you!" Just beyond the dwarf, a huge shadow with many-faceted, pale eyes has arisen out of nowhere. Bain turns; his crystal reveals a sickening spider-beast just as it knocks him into the pit. Then it comes at you!

You raise your weapon in time to meet its lunge, but the spider is irresistible, moving upon you with its great bulk. Bain, in a clatter, scrambles out of the filth to attack the beast from the side.

You are engaged in combat.

(**GIANT SPIDER** OB:5 DB:4 EP:50)

- *If you successfully Run Away,* ***turn to 313.***
- *If you increase the spider's Damage Taken to 40 or more without killing it or exceeding the EP limit of 50,* ***turn to 388.***
- *If you defeat the spider,* ***turn to 368.***
- *If the spider defeats you,* ***turn to 194.***

5

190 **Time: 5**

After forcing your way through the bent portcullis and walking down a short corridor, you come to an excellent example of dwarvish stonework: a wide bridge over a black chasm. The chasm is probably not bottomless, but then you cannot be sure. The walk is build of solid grey rock and looks as if it were carved out of the mountain in one great piece. No railing or kerb flanks the span.

- *If you cross the bridge,* ***turn to 126.***
- *If you return to the last intersection,* ***turn to 211.***

191 **Time: 5**

Within the box, a small blue diamond flashes in the half-light. It is unset, though finely crafted. *If you keep the Blue Diamond, enter it on your Character Record.* ***Turn to 307.***

192 **Time: 5**

"You are well-suited to this work, Bain. I think you should go first, but be careful. I will follow."

Skeptically, Bain eyes the crack, then hoists himself up into it. By the light of the crystal he carries around his neck, you see his form slowly receding. Then you follow. The sides of the fissure quickly close in upon you, and being rough, they scrape your hands and shoulders. Loose gravel slides under your feet. ***Pick a number*** *and add your Perception bonus:*

- *If 2-7,* ***turn to 193.***
- *If 8-12,* ***turn to 196.***

193 **Time: 0**

Much to your surprise, a slithering arm comes up from behind and grasps your leg! You are being dragged back out into the cave. "Bain!" you cry out to alert the dwarf. With a tumble, you are dragged out onto the cave floor. *Note that in the following combat you are Surprised.* ***Turn to 199.***

194 **Time: N/A**

During the heated battle, you feel a cruel stinger pierce you, and you know that you have been injected with a foul and deadly poison. Eyes rolling into the back of your head, you hear Bain calling, but his voice seems far away. All goes black, and you remember no more. Your quest has come to a sad conclusion. **The End.**

195 **Time: 0**

The cabinet holds four large drawers stacked one atop the other, and one set of standing doors. Each drawer is decorated with delicate carvings of flowers and inlaid with thin gold wire. *You may examine each receptacle only once.*

- *If you open the top drawer,* ***turn to 233.***
- *If you open the second drawer,* ***turn to 117.***
- *If you open the third drawer,* ***turn to 341.***
- *If you open the fourth drawer,* ***turn to 261.***
- *If you open the set of doors,* ***turn to 307.***
- *Otherwise,* ***move on*** *to any "A" Location.*

196 **Time: 0**

Something is slithering up behind you! You turn in the confined space but see nothing clearly in the darkness and shadow. Then you feel a cold and clammy arm grasp your leg. "Bain!" you shout. "Something has got a hold..." You trail off as the clutching arm drags you back down the crack to the cave floor. ***Turn to 199.***

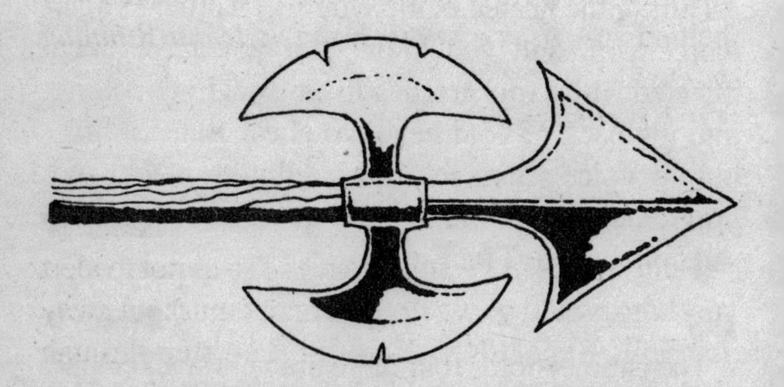

197 **Time: 5**

As you run headlong into the gloom, leaping over ill-repaired and crumbling stonework, a terrifying sound comes up from behind then surrounds you with its eerie echoes. War-drums beat a steady 'Thrum, thrum,' and are answered by others in the distance: 'Thrum, thrum!'

Bain calls up to you, "We have awakened all the orcs of Moria! Run faster. They are close behind us!"

The ledge breaks into a set of shallow stairs which lead up, and these you take two at a time with Bain at your heals. The wall of the rift at this point has closed to within a mere hundred feet of the opposite side. Sallow orcs across the gulf see you, crying out to their fellows and lofting darts at your flying shadows. Arrows snap as they strike the rock at your shoulder or the stairs at your feet! The fastest goblins have now begun to climb the stairway behind you. ***Pick a number*** *and add your Running bonus:*

- *If 2-7,* ***turn to 376.***
- *If 8-12,* ***turn to 383.***

198 **Time: 10**

Bain speaks in a wary whisper: "So as not to alert any who would be waiting beyond, I must put away the light. Stay close." You and Bain step through and shut the door behind you. ***Turn to 179.***

199 **Time: 5**

The water of the pool is boiling and seething, and from it emerges a multitude of grey, slick tentacles that even now reach for you. Drawing forth your weapon, you prepare to strike them.

You must fight this watery horror and you may not Run Away.

(WATER CREATURE OB:7 DB:0 EP:40)

- *If you have not defeated the creature after three rounds of combat,* ***turn to 209.***
- *Otherwise:*
  - *If you defeat the creature,* ***turn to 216.***
  - *If the creature defeats you,* ***turn to 215.***

200 **Time: 0**

You see something glitter from beneath the pallet. Bending down, you see that a bright ring has been hidden or misplaced there.

Intrigued, Bain asks: "What have you found?"

"Let us have a closer look," you respond. ***Pick a number:***

- *If 2-7,* ***turn to 393.***
- *If 8-12,* ***turn to 400.***

201 **Time: 0**

"Do you know what it is?" you ask.

"It is special, but I know little else." answers Bain.

"Special or not, it is of no use to me. Do you want to keep it?"

Bain haughtily replies, "All I want is the Will, and we will not find it here." ***Turn to 384.***

202 **Time: N/A**

You are cruelly slain at the hands of a terrifying Naugrim. Moria is your tomb; your quest comes to a sad conclusion just on the verge of success. **The End.**

203 **Time: 240**

Wandering many cobwebbed passages and taking twisting stairways illuminated only by the faint radiance of Bain's amulet, you and the quiet dwarf come to a wide hall. It lies in decay now, with the ugly leavings of orcs evident. Just as you are about to suggest a hurried retreat, three orcs appear through the doorway you had just used to enter the hall. Scimitars raised, they howl and charge. Drawing your weapon, you engage two of the orcs, while Bain hurriedly prepares to counter the third.

Note that in the following melee, you may not Run Away.

(**ORC#1** OB:1 DB:2 EP:20)
(**ORC#2** OB:1 DB:1 EP:13)

- *If you defeat both orcs,* ***turn to 176.***
- *If an orc defeats you,* ***turn to 278.***

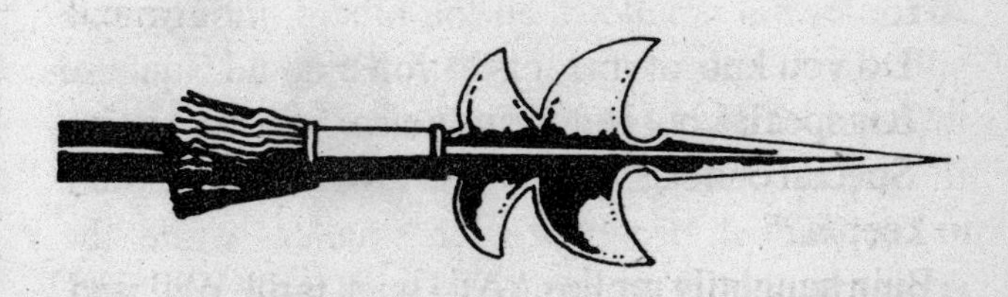

204 **Time: 0**

Finding nothing useful, you decide to continue your search elsewhere. Bain follows. ***Move on*** *to any "A" Location.*

205 **Time: 5**

Both you and Bain enter a storeroom. As you examine the shelves, a large snake drops from above. Wrapping itself around you like a constrictor, it begins to squeeze! Bain gives a shout, and jumping to your side he tries to remove the beast, though he cannot strike at it for fear of hurting you.

You must fight the Cave Snake. In the following combat you are Surprised and may not Run Away.

(**CAVE SNAKE** OB:2 DB:0 EP:10)

- *If you defeat the snake,* ***turn to 225.***
- *If the snake defeats you,* ***turn to 300.***

206 **Time: 10** **Exp Pt: 10**

You dodge the hammer as it flies up toward you and breaks upon the wall behind with a thunderous splintering. The troll picks up another rock and advances, but you and the dwarf have already ducked into another passage. Fortunately, this one is somewhat smaller than the others, though you still think one of the cave-trolls could squeeze through. "This is good," says Bain who is managing to keep up. "We can move faster than they in here."

The tunnel becomes ever smaller, while the scraping pursuit of the trolls falls farther behind, until they can no longer be heard. ***Turn to 184.***

207 **Time: 5**

The wily orc is aware of your approach. As you step forward, he draws his sword with a practised movement and leaps toward you with a snarl. As he attacks, you can see his face clearly. Large teeth, more like tusks than human teeth, curve out from under his upper lip, and his eyes are set in deep folds of blackened skin. He cries something in a harsh tongue as his sword cuts through the air. "This one is mine!" you call back to the dwarf.

(**ORC** OB:1 DB:1 EP: 18)

- *If you successfully Run Away,* ***turn to 160.***
- *If you defeat the orc,* ***turn to 386.***
- *If the orc defeats you,* ***turn to 135.***

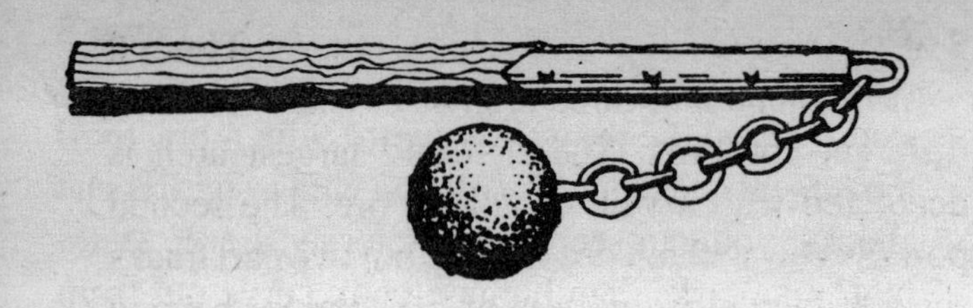

208 **Time: 0**

You are hit in the leg by an orcish dart. ***Pick a number twice,*** *add the results together, then increase your Damage Taken by that amount.*

- *If your Damage Taken now exceeds your Endurance value,* ***turn to 226.***
- *Otherwise,* **pick a number** *and add your General bonus:*
  - *If 2-5,* ***turn to 226.***
  - *If 6-12,* ***turn to 263.***

209 **Time: 0** **Exp Pt: 10**

You have hacked at the tough hide of the hideous arms, but to no avail. Then Bain finally springs down from the crevasse, wielding his axe. Leaping to your side, he hews two of the tentacles with one swing, and so frees your upper body from the crushing grasp of your foe. Then the two of you strike at the other appendages which hold your legs, eventually forcing them to releasing you. The hideous tentacles retreat back into the pool, silently slipping beneath the surface. Soon the water is still once more, though now stained with a foul ichor. ***Turn to 217.***

210 **Time: 0**

At this junction, three archways lead into three different corridors. The first and largest arch is decorated with a vein of golden ore. The second portalway is without decoration, but two cart tracks run parallel down one side of the corridor beyond the portal. The third displays a small rune composed of green crystal shards embedded in the stone.

- *If you go through the golden ore archway,* ***turn to 240.***
- *If you go through the green rune archway,* ***turn to 283.***
- *If you enter the cart track tunnel,* ***turn to 187.***

211 **Time: 0**

From this intersection, the corridor to the southeast is partially blocked by a fallen portcullis, but the metal gate is bent, and there is room to squeeze through.

The corridor to the northeast has four steps leading up into the darkness. The steps are carved with runes which appear to be simply decorative.

The east passage was at sometime blocked by a huge boulder dropped from a trap above, but a space has been cleared away around it. The passage is crudely carved, surely "the work of orcs," as Bain derisively notes.

- *If you take the east passage,* ***turn to 370.***
- *If you take the southeast passage,* ***turn to 190.***
- *If you take the northeast passage,* ***turn to 269.***

9

212 **Time: 0**

You stand in the room, an old dwelling of some sort. It appears deserted. Although the belongings lie scattered, you see little of the wanton destruction which characterizes orcish habitation. The room contains what is left of a fine rug, a few chairs, small table, and a hardwood chest. Bain seems most intrigued by the chest.

- *If you want to open the chest,* ***turn to 305.***
- *If you leave,* ***turn to 250.***

213 **Time: 0** **Exp Pt: 2**

"Kill it!" whispers Bain. Quick as thought, you hit the back of your hand against the cabinet, giving yourself a nasty bruise but disposing of the spider. You have saved yourself from a deadly bite! ***Turn to 195.***

214 **Time: 10**

Although it was difficult, for the lock was old and stiff, you successfully unlock the chest. "Well, open it!" says Bain. ***Pick a number*** *and add your Perception bonus:*

- *If 2-6,* ***turn to 382.***
- *If 7-12,* ***turn to 237.***

215 **Time: N/A**

Before Bain arrives to help, the horror from the pool has squeezed you into unconsciousness. The last sensation you have is that of slipping beneath the surface of the pool; being enveloped by cool, silent water. Your quest has come to a sad conclusion. **The End.**

216 **Time: 0** **Exp Pt: 40**

Before Bain arrives to help, you dispatch the terrible arms from the pool, having severed several of them. The rest, both whole, and wounded, withdraw back beneath the surface, leaving behind a trail of foul ichor.

When Bain finally does arrive, the last of the pale tentacles that lay at your feet end their helpless writhing.

"What was it?" queries the dwarf, though the remnants of the beast are plain to see.

"Some wicked thing that gnaws at the roots of the world." ***Turn to 217.***

217 **Time: 5**

Bain asks you a question with concern in his voice, though he would have you think he speaks in jest. "Has the creature left you in one piece?"

"I feel fit enough," you say. "This place is wicked though. Let us return to the main tunnel and continue that way. I care not that it dips into water. Nothing there could be as horrible as what has discovered us here."

Bain agrees. "That would be just as well. Before you were dragged out, I saw the end of the fissure — we cannot go that way." So it is that the two of you leave the cave and its deadly silent pool.

Turn to 175.

218 **Time: 0**

You turn within the confined space of the fissure and make your way back out into the cave.
Turn to 220.

219 **Time: 5**

The drawer is empty of everything but dust. Bain sneezes mightily and the sound takes some moments to die. *Turn to 384.*

220 **Time: 5**

You are confronted by a horrifying sight. Writhing on the floor of the cave is Bain, and about him are wrapped a multitude of slick and luminous grey tentacles dragging him towards the pool, now a black boiling froth. Drawing your weapon, you jump forth to hack at one of the wet arms, but as you do so, many others come up from the water to grasp at you too!

"What foul creature is this!" you cry, preparing your strike. But before you do, your legs are entangled by two of the clutching arms.

You must fight the tentacles, and you may not Run Away.

(**WATER CREATURE** OB:6 DB:0 EP:30)

- *If you defeat the creature,* ***turn to 224.***
- *If the creature defeats you,* ***turn to 223.***

221 **Time: 0**

Something swoops down from out of the darkness. *Note that in the following combat, you are Surprised.* ***Turn to 127.***

222 **Time: 10**

The cave entrance is not dwarf-made, that is clear; rather, it is simply a rent in the fabric of the mountain. A breeze comes out of it, bearing a faint, bitter odour. As you slip inside, Bain brings forth his amulet. The soft sphere of light is reassuring, but you still cannot see deep within. This cavern must have been torn open by some shifting of the mountain long after Durin's Folk were driven from Moria. ***Pick a number*** *and add your Perception bonus:*

- *If 2-5,* ***turn to 246.***
- *If 6-12,* ***turn to 363.***

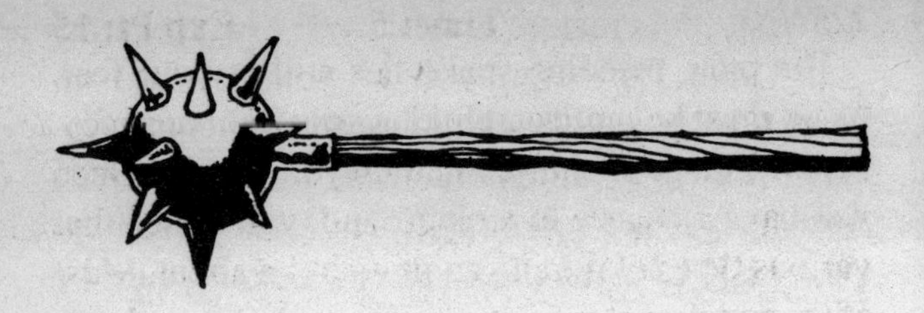

223 **Time: N/A**

The gripping tentacles rend your limbs and choke the breath out of you. You succumb to the enveloping darkness and the last thing you feel is cool water washing over your body as you slip beneath the surface of the pool. Your quest has come to a sad conclusion. **The End.**

224 **Time: 10** **Exp Pt: 30**

With a final, mighty strike, you hack off one of the beast's thicker arms. The others snake back into the water, leaving you and Bain gasping for breath at the edge of the pool. Your companion is hurt, but seems strong enough to stand, though it takes him some time to do so. "Let us be gone from this wretched place," says Bain. "I care not if the fissure or the tunnel leads the right way."

You share the dwarf's mind, so as soon as you both are able, you make your way out to the main corridor and turn to follow that way. When you see that the passage dips and is at least partially filled with stagnant water, Bain motions for you to lead the way, though he asks for his crystal back first. ***Turn to 175.***

225 **Time: 5** **Exp Pt: 15**

The pale, bleeding snake lies still at your feet. "You must be more careful," warns Bain unnecessarily. You nod grimly, catching your breath. Once you have a chance to look around, you notice that various types of mining equipment lie about. Most of the equipment is carefully laid on shelves or hung on the wall. But in one corner of the room rests a pile of dirty picks and rusty shovels which Bain examines. It looks as if the dwarves who once worked here were too hurried in their departure to take proper care of these.

"There is nothing here for us," says Bain. Agreeing, the two of you leave the room.

- *If you wish to explore the north-east passage,* ***turn to 286.***
- *If you return down the west passage,* ***turn to 328.***

226 **Time: N/A**

Wounded and knocked off balance, you lose your grip on the climbing-hold above. You fall backwards into the black pit below and know no more of Middle-earth. Your quest has come to a sad conclusion. **The End.**

227 **Time: 10**

You travel down a mossy, damp corridor to a junction. From the moss on the walls grow small blue flowers which smell tart and seem to have their own inner light. The east-to-west passageway you are traveling along divides into two corridors, one heading northeast and the other southeast. You strain to hear watery sounds coming from the northeast corridor, while Bain indicates that a wooden door stands at the end of the southeast corridor.

- *If you go southeast,* ***turn to 241.***
- *If you go northeast,* ***turn to 286.***
- *If you return to the west,* ***turn to 328.***

228 **Time: 0**

Indeed, light-stones can be seen just under the surface of the pool, not more than an arm's reach away. They are scattered in a loose pile, but though they cast their light, it does not penetrate far into the murky depths further on.

- *If you decide to return to the main corridor outside the cave and continue that way,* ***turn to 175.***
- *If you gather the loose light-stones,* ***turn to 247.***

229 **Time: 5**

You recognize the nut as one having special healing capabilities. *If you keep the Nut, enter it on your Character Record. When eaten, it will decrease your Damage Taken by 10.* ***Turn to 384.***

230 **Time: 15**

What begins as a finely-honed dwarvish passage degenerates into a rude, twisting tunnel. "Even the roughest of dwarf-passages would not be left long in a state like this," says Bain.

You find yourself on the verge of entering a convoluted criss-crossing of tunnels, many of which you guess open into ill-hewn grottos.

- *If you continue,* ***turn to 275.***
- *If you return to the last junction,* ***turn to 103.***

231 **Time: 5**

From the shadow cast by a pillar to your left steps a dwarf! Clad in mail and helm, he is a fearsome sight, if somewhat expected. Then to your right, another dwarf moves into view. "It seems we have found the dwarves, or they have found us," you say to Bain, "though I doubt it will be a happy meeting."

Then to the first dwarf, you raise your voice and challenge him; "Who comes upon us so — unawares and with weapons bared? Speak!"

"Do not play the fool," he growls from under a reddish beard. "You are here for the Will, and so are we, but it is we who shall have it. Now tell us were it is!"

Bain pulls the axe from his belt and steps forward. "You may kill me and you still shall not discover where the Will can be found. Only I know, and I will not say!"

11

Then the first dwarf too takes a step ahead and comes close to Bain. He begins to speak in the secret tongue of the dwarves, Khuzdul, at first quietly, then ending with a shout. Bain responds in kind, and it sounds as if the two are trading uncouth insults. The first dwarf shifts the axe in his hands just before Bain takes a mighty swing with his! Battle is joined; there is no stopping them. The second dwarf raises his weapon and charges you with a yell.

You must fight this dwarf and may not Run Away.
(**DWARF** OB:4 DB:3 EP:30)

- *If you defeat the dwarf,* ***turn to 297.***
- *If the dwarf knocks you unconscious,* ***turn to 158.***
- *If the dwarf kills you,* ***turn to 202.***

232 **Time: 0** **Exp Pt: 45**

The fight is bloody, and the dwarves ask no quarter. You are forced to slay your opponent as Bain takes his.

When the deeds are done and the two agents lay still at your feet, you ask Bain who they were.

"As we had suspected, they were Bror's cousins. They must have left the camp shortly after we, then come to Moria before us. But this is a sad day — as it should be when dwarf is forced to kill dwarf. There are precious few of us left in the world as it is."

"This is behind us now," you say. "We must still get the Will to your uncle." Bain takes a last look at his dead kinsmen, then removes the rune-key from a pocket. ***Turn to 413.***

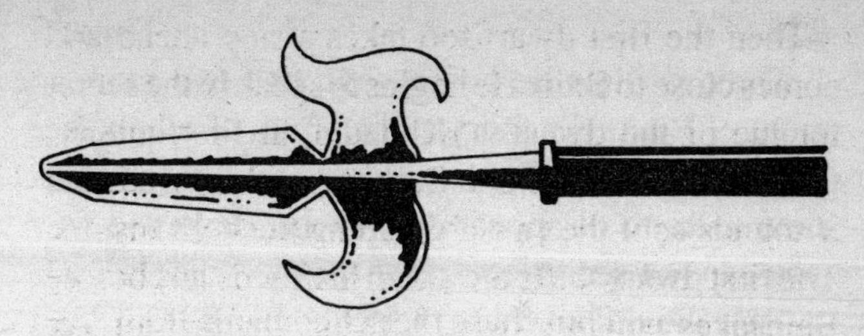

233 **Time: 5**

You slowly open the drawer but find it empty.

"We will not find the Will in this place. Let us be off!" advises Bain. ***Turn to 195.***

234 **Time: 5**

"No!" you say to Bain with conviction. "Let us dispatch them here so they cannot follow."

"Fool!" answers the dwarf. "There are too many — it is too late!" Out of the darkness rush several orcs brandishing curved swords and howling in frenzy. Three set upon Bain, while an equal number attack you.

You must fight these foul creatures from the pits of Khazad-dûm.

(**ORC #1** OB:4 DB:1 EP:30)
(**ORC #2** OB:2 DB:1 EP:20)
(**ORC #3** OB:1 DB:0 EP:13)

Award yourself 18 Experience Points for each orc that you defeat.

- *If you successfully Run Away,* ***turn to 403.***
- *If you defeat all three of the orcs,* ***turn to 235.***
- *If you are defeated by any of the orcs,* ***turn to 258.***

Three goblins lie before you, and two more in front of Bain. His third, and a group of others that had not advanced, run towards the back of the cave, then seem to disappear down some darkened way you can not see.

"We should not chase them," councils Bain, "but rather get away while we can. They will be back with greater numbers."

You agree with the dwarf and step back out onto the ledge overlooking the bottomless, coal-black chasm. But just then another group of armoured goblins, numbering twenty or more, come into view from around the bend in the path behind, some carrying torches. When they see the two of you standing there, they raise a battle cry and rush with scimitars bared.

"We cannot prevail against such numbers!" says Bain at your side, "Quickly, this way!" He bounds off along the ledge in the opposite direction. With longer strides, you pass the dwarf — though that is dangerous — and hold the crystal ahead of you. ***Turn to 197.***

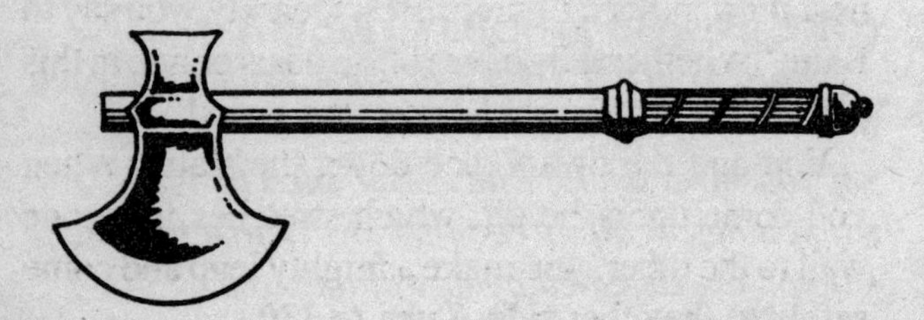

You pat Bain lightly on the shoulder, then indicate the orc nearby. The dwarf nods in understanding and silently hefts up his axe, ready for the attack. A brief moment passes. Then, in a sudden fury, Bain cries out "Moria!" and sets upon the dark figure.

The orc whirls to meet Bain's onslaught, catching the down-swinging axe blade with the hilt of his black scimitar, just drawn. A ringing 'clang' echoes throughout the great cavern. The orc howls and brings his own weapon around in a low swing. This Bain deflects with his haft, then knees his foe in the stomach. The orc emits a pained grunt and loses his balance, tumbling backwards. In a clatter of armour and weapons, the orc falls down the stairs. As he reaches the bottom with Bain in pursuit, some weight of stone gives way with a rumble. A pit trap at the bottom of the stair has swallowed the goblin!

As you reach the flight of stairs and look down into the darkness, Bain approaches. "If only we had an orc for each trap we will come upon! There, at the stair's foot, the orc fell into a hidden pit."

Behind you, from the other side of the cavern, you hear the approach of more orcs. Quickly, you say to Bain: "Whether they have followed us or live in this place, I do wish to ask! Down the stairs!"

You and the dwarf race down the stairs. When you come upon the pit, which stretches from one wall to the other, you make a mighty leap and come safely to the other side. ***Turn to 330.***

6

237 **Time: 10** **Exp Pt: 5**

You realize that the chest has a trap which was activated when the lock mechanism was disengaged. Now, several short needles protrude from the lock and opening latch. "Poisoned needles," warns Bain. "Do not touch them."

You both decide it would be best to leave the chest alone at this point, for you cannot guess what other horrors await within. Leaving the room, you soon arrive at the corridor junction again. ***Turn to 120.***

238 **Time: 0**

As you are halfway across, a section of the bridge falls away from underneath you! Bain emits a wild cry at your side. ***Pick a number*** *and add your General bonus:*

- *If 2-9,* ***turn to 153.***
- *If 10-12,* ***turn to 289.***

239 **Time: 5**

Off the main passageway a cave opens to your left. It looks forbiddingly dark; no light-stones illuminate the interior, though you guess it is fairly large.

"What say you to this, dwarf?" you ask. "Again it is not shown on this... your family's map."

Bain replies, "The map shows a corridor, and that is what we must follow. Agreed?"

- *If you enter the cave,* ***turn to 222.***
- *If you continue down the corridor,* ***turn to 122.***

240 **Time: 15**

You walk beneath the archway containing the vein of gold and pass into the dwarf-hewn corridor. Red light-stones in simple patterns provide dim but sufficient lighting. You soon come to another junction. ***Turn to 120.***

241 **Time: 5**

The corridor comes to a wooden door. The door, despite its lock, stands ajar.

- *If you enter and search the room,* ***turn to 205.***
- *If you explore the north-east corridor instead,* ***turn to 286.***
- *If you return down the west corridor,* ***turn to 328.***

242 **Time: N/A**

The collapsing ceiling piles tons of stone upon you and the dwarf! Escape is impossible; Moria becomes your tomb. **The End.**

243 **Time: 0**

Indeed, light-stones can be seen just under the surface of the pool, not more than an arm's reach away. They are scattered in a loose pile, but though they cast their light, it does not penetrate far into the murky depths further on. You are about to dip your hand in to gather some of the stones, when slow waves lap up against your feet. There has been a disturbance, like a long oily ripple which started further out toward the middle of the pool.

- *If you decide to return to the main corridor outside the cave and continue down that way,* ***turn to 175.***
- *If you gather the loose light-stones,* ***turn to 247.***

244 **Time: 15**

You reason your course of action. "Well, we cannot swim to the Will, nor do I think the fissure will lead to a good end. The corridor outside too seems cursed with water. I say we should take a closer look at the tunnel back there. What say you, dwarf?"

Bain looks over at you, the worry plane on his face. "At first I would say we play out the main tunnel, but this one may suit us fine. Let us go." With that, the two of you skirt the pool to the left and head back toward the tunnel opening leading deeper into the unknown depths of Moria.

Once inside and traveling down the sloping passage, you chance some conversation despite the deadly silence. "Bain, is this dwarf-work?"

"I would say so, though it is not finished, of course. Possibly they were planning to delve a mine here." After walking on a short way, the dwarf corrects himself. "Not a mine. Notice how the passage now dips and twists? Maybe they were just expanding some steam tunnel or chute."

Then the two of you notice that side corridors not only branch off this way and that, but the tunnel splits in several places too. Sometimes the ceiling stoops low so that you are both forced to bend over, while at other times it slants, dives and even drops away at your feet.

Then Bain speaks. "I question the wisdom of this course now. If we continue any further, I am sure we will lose our way. Even now I am forgetting the way we came." His voice falls dead upon the close walls of the tunnel.

"I too am unsure of the way," you admit.

- *If you turn back and make your way out to the main tunnel you were traveling before you entered the previous cave,* ***turn to 180.***
- *If you turn back and make you way to the pool in the last cave,* ***turn to 181.***
- *If you turn back and make your way to the fissure in the last cave,* ***turn to 185.***
- *If you continue traveling deeper into these tunnels,* ***turn to 377.***

245 **Time: 0**

Leaving the pouch where it rests, you carefully close the drawer. ***Turn to 195.***

246 **Time: 0**

You move forward toward what you think is the centre of the cave while Bain's amulet shows only the grey stone floor. "I doubt that we will find the Will in here," complains the dwarf. "Please, let us stop this foolishness and go."

- *If you continue to explore the cave,* ***turn to 221.***
- *If you leave the cave and continue up the main corridor you were traveling,* ***turn to 122.***

247 **Time: 0**

You make to reach for the seductive stones when Bain catches your shoulder. "Wait!" his voice is low but urgent. "I do not like the look of this; some devilry is afoot here."

Pulling your arm away from his grasp, you say, "In every pit, an orc; around every corner, a troll. That is the way of it for you, Bain. But I do not fear the black pool; it is quiet and safe. Now if you do not mind, I will gather some of these light-stones for myself. They will be useful." You turn to retrieve the crystals. ***Turn to 254.***

248 **Time: N/A**

Running through the dark woods, you lead Bain back to the bridge at a breathless pace. The young dwarf is tireless! The pursuing elven archers pause at the bridge and allow you and Bain to race across the swift Celebrant unharmed.

Once across the river, you pause to catch your wind. Then you curse and declare: "From now on, you do as I say, dwarf!" Sliding down the river bank, you take a great mouthful of cool, clear water. "Let us be off now! And no more trouble from you, Bain." ***Turn to 251.***

249 **Time: N/A**

A cruel orcish blow takes your feet out from under you, and with a crash, you land on the cave floor. You reach up to get help from Bain, but he is sorely engaged. Then you feel grasping claws grip your legs and arms. The orcs are dragging you away!

The next sensation you have is that of foul orc-breath hot upon your face. Wicked words are uttered, but you cannot tell what the creature is saying. Then you see a great, bristled arm holding a curved blade. It slashes down toward you; after a stabbing pain you feel no more. Your quest has come to a grim conclusion. **The End.**

250 **Time: 5**

You decide that the room holds nothing of interest and turn back. Soon you return to the corridor junction. ***Turn to 120.***

251 **Time: Special**

Walking the thirty-five leagues to the Dimrill Dale proves to be a silent and safe journey of many days. You come to think of the songs of birds and the chatter of squirrels as welcome companionship, for Bain says nothing but "Bah!" and "Faster!" (His mood has been slow to change since Lórien.)

By your reckoning, you will have two days inside Moria to discover the whereabouts of the Will — if it still exists. That, in addition to the twelve days journeying there and back, will constitute the fourteen days allowed by Bror.

This morning, the massive peak of the Silvertine juts heavenward, now seemingly just ahead of you. The dwarf increases his pace, as if under an enchantment. Then the climb turns steep as you leave behind the birches and fir-trees of the forest and enter the rugged, rocky foothills of the eastern Misty Mountains. The ancient stone dwarf-road beside the narrowing river leads into the highlands; the Mirrormere must be close at hand! *Note on your Character Record that the Time is now 0 Minutes of Day 7. Reduce the number of meals entered on your Character Record by 6.* **Turn to 291.**

252 **Time: 0**

"What is it used for?" you ask the dwarf.

"I have no useful idea," replies Bain. "Perhaps it is a secret long since lost." Leaving the pouch, you close the drawer. ***Turn to 195.***

253 **Time: 0**

With a terrifying rumble, a deadfall has been released from above; you have set off one of the fabled ceiling traps of Moria! ***Pick a number*** *and add your Running bonus:*

- *If 2-7,* ***turn to 242.***
- *If 8-12,* ***turn to 133.***

254 **Time: 0**

Suddenly, the dark waters begin to seethe and boil. Then, with a great commotion and erupting fountain of spray, a multitude of thick arms, like tentacles burst forth! ***Pick a number*** *and add your Perception bonus:*

- *If 2-7,* ***turn to 260.***
- *If 8-12,* ***turn to 259.***

255 **Time: 0**

"There are orcs here — many of them." Your voice is a silent wraith that soon dies.

"Do we stand and fight, or run?" Bain asks urgently. "Be quick!"

- *If you try to run back out of the cave,* ***turn to 265.***
- *If you hold your ground,* ***turn to 358.***

256 **Time: 0**

As you and the dwarf rush for the black crack at the end of the cavern, another orcish figure looms out of the darkness to block your path! He seems to have been taken by surprise — you lift an elbow to catch him in the jaw as you run up. Crunch! You send the guard flying against the cave wall, head thrown back. ***Turn to 160.***

257 **Time: 5**

You fight these degenerated remnants of the Balrog's army.

(**ORC #1** OB:1 DB:1 EP:10)
(**ORC #2** OB:2 DB:2 EP:15)
(**ORC #3** OB:3 DB:1 EP:20)

- *If you successfully Run Away,* ***turn to 335.***
- *If you defeat these three orcs,* ***turn to 137.***
- *If you are defeated by any of the orcs,* ***turn to 249.***

258 **Time: N/A**

You are knocked down by the flat swing of an orcish blade, but you are soon set upon by closely wielded knives. The orcs take no prisoners and Bain too is brought down. Your quest comes to a sad conclusion deep within the Mines of Moria. **The End.**

259 **Time: 5**

The tentacles, wet luminous grey strands, grasp at you and the dwarf who is already brandishing his axe. You must fight this water horror.

(**WATER CREATURE** OB:6 DB:0 EP:20)

- *If you successfully Run Away,* ***turn to 288.***
- *If you defeat the creature,* ***turn to 266.***
- *If the creature defeats you,* ***turn to 285.***

260 **Time: 0**

You and Bain stagger back, shocked by the unearthly sight. *In the following combat, you are Surprised.* ***Turn to 259.***

261 **Time: 5**

You open the drawer and finding it empty, begin prodding along the back of it to reveal any concealed compartments. But there is something on your hand! Withdrawing, you see that it is a singularly huge spider with long, hairy legs and a grey diamond marking on its back. ***Pick a number*** *and add your General bonus:*

- *If 2-8,* ***turn to 279.***
- *If 9-12,* ***turn to 213.***

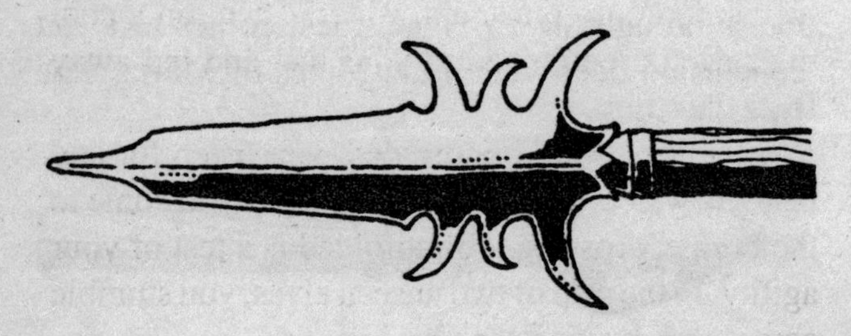

262 **Time: N/A**

Grabbed from behind, you and Bain are quickly overcome by the stealthy, powerful elves. Bound and blindfolded, you are hurried unceremoniously along a path deeper into the woods. By the rising and setting of the sun, you realize that you and the dwarf have been held for at least two days and nights, fed only bread and water. Then, on a cool night, you are dragged to your feet and led away from the camp.

Traveling south, blindfolded, you listen for and hear the waters of the Celebrant. Soon you come to the bridge; crossing it blindfolded is a test of your agility. In the grip of two unseen elves, you stumble across the swaying rope bridge.

7

The night is a long one; trudging without pause, you ache to rest and drink some clear, cool water. As morning breaks and a faint light slips under the blindfold, you hear the measured breathing of Bain a few steps behind you. Suddenly, you are spun around and the blindfold is removed. Blinking, you face a pair of fair Wood- elves in forest tunics, their dark hair shimmering in the sunlight. Without a word, the leader indicates the camp no more than a furlong ahead. Your belongings — and Bain — are dumped on the ground at your feet. Without a sound, they disappear into the woods along the river.

"Thank you very much," you say snidely to the Dwarf, reaching for your weapons and haversack. Bain carefully brushes himself off and gathers his things. "Come, let's explain our great success to your uncle." Together you trudge wearily into the camp where the adventure began and shamefacedly confess your failure to Bror and his kinsmen. Amidst his ringing curses and oaths, you vow to do things differently next time — if you get the chance. **The End.**

263 **Time: 5**

Disregarding the pain of the wound, you continue to climb — following the path of the dwarf. Lithe orcs now follow up behind, but you make it to the landing where Bain now stands before they reach you. For his part, the dwarf has prepared his own bow. ***Turn to 353.***

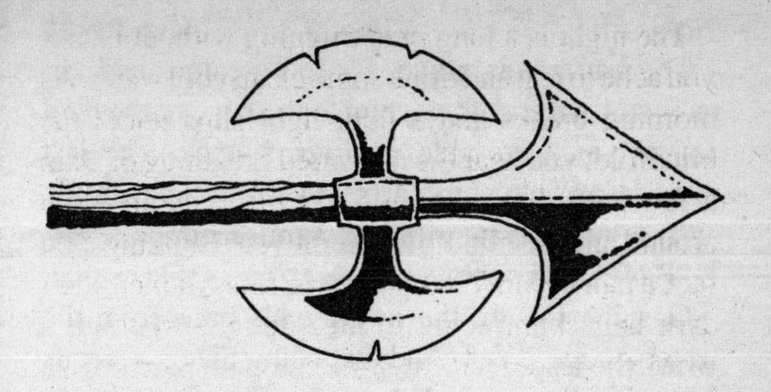

264 **Time: 10**

The tunnel now comes level and then begins an ascent. At one point, a reddish mist falls from the ceiling, betraying the presence of deadly, sleep-inducing Gorfang. Aware of the dangerous properties of the moss, you and Bain avoid the overhead niche where it grows. Once past it, Bain says, "Now it is but a short way to the Great Hall. May no ill fortune bar the way." ***Turn to 392.***

265 **Time: 0**

"Fly!" you call out, hoping Bain will be quick to follow. From behind, a glimmering lights your escape. Bain has again brought forth the amulet, but the sight it reveals is grave. Black orcs have circled behind and in front, nearly blocking your only escape. You draw your weapon and charge as the foul creatures hoot and howl and gnashing their broken teeth. ***Take an action:***

- *If you successfully Run Away,* ***turn to 335.***
- *If you Attack,* ***turn to 257.***

266 **Time: 5** **Exp Pt: 25**

The battle was grave, for the creature had entangled Bain and drawn him to the edge of the pool before you were able to drive it back. The last remnants of clutching arms now slip beneath the surface of the water, trailing a foul ichor.

"Bain, can you travel?"

Gasping for air, the dwarf reels back from the water's edge. "Yes. And that being the case, let us leave this place, for whatever that thing was, it may return more determined at any time!" Though you are not sure that this might be the case, you side with the dwarf and decide to leave the cave altogether.

After a short time, the two of you emerge at the main passage, where you continue your journey searching for a new way to Old Bror's Great Hall. As you had discerned before, the tunnel dips down and becomes at least half filled with water. Although you are loathe to enter, it seems you have little choice. ***Turn to 175.***

267 **Time: 5**

Bain discovers the trap which guards this span and says, "We will be safe if we pass on the left side. I will lead, you follow."

"Very well," you reply, "let us be off and meet what, or who, we may." ***Move on** to B1 (The Great Hall).*

268 **Time: 0**

Across the dark chasm you can just discern some movement along what you would guess to be another walking-ledge. A hidden flicker of fire-light shows some skulking creature, but at this distance, you cannot be certain of what it is.

Then sounds, muted and confused by the distance, come to you. Orc-speech! "Bain, there are orcs on the other side, but I cannot judge the distance."

"I see some of them," he says. "They are level with us, but it must be several hundred feet across to the other side. They may see us standing here. We should be off!" ***Turn to 411.***

269 **Time: 10**

You come to an arching stone bridge over a broad, dark chasm with no discernible bottom. You consider tossing a small rock in to see if you can hear it land, but that has started trouble in the past, and you are not interested in making the same mistake.

You study your map which shows a bridge, but you have no way of knowing if this is the same one. "Why did the dwarves of Moria build their bridges without railings?" you ask, not expecting a reply.

"Answer me this first," says Bain. "Do you walk with your feet or your hands?" You must admit the dwarf makes disturbing sense, after his own fashion. ***Turn to 129.***

270 **Time: 10**

You plan to sell the mithril coat to Bror. But first, you must open the case without setting off any traps. And traps you reckon there are. Huffing and puffing indignantly, Bain backs away, clearly disapproving of what you are about to do. "Indeed, it is valuable," says Bain, "but to lose it now would be a grave injustice to all the Dwarves of Middle-earth, particularly the children of Durin!" His pleas come too late however, as you have already begun to lift the case. ***Pick a number*** *and add your Trickery bonus:*

- *If 2-11,* ***turn to 173.***
- *If 12,* ***turn to 373.***

271 **Time: N/A**

Unwilling to risk yourself in the forest of Lórien, you turn and walk back to the bridge. ***Pick a number:***

- *If 2-8,* ***turn to 311.***
- *If 9-12,* ***turn to 315.***

272 **Time: 10**

You walk down a passageway of elegant stonework, unsure if this is indeed the corridor indicated on Bror's map. The design on the walls changes every so often, with a smooth vertical band of polished stone dividing the different patterns. You see examples of axe head and diamond designs produced in dozens of different colours and types of stone.

Ultimately you come to another junction. "Confound it!" exclaims Bain. You enter under an arch having two-foot high niches within which are alabaster shards, the remains of statues or vases perhaps. ***Turn to 103.***

273 **Time: N/A**

When you awaken into the gloom of the Great Hall, you find Bain cruelly slain beside you and the other dwarves nowhere in sight. The rune-key is gone, and you suspect that the Will is too. Sadly, your quest comes to a sad conclusion, for though you eventually find a way out of Moria, you do not find Bror, nor do you ever hear of him again. **The End.**

274 **Time: 10**

You come to what you think might be the entrance to the Great Hall of Bror's family, but instead first discover a vast cavern. Above you, light enters from a broad shaft leading out to the mountain's slope. The dwarves you saw before are not visible here.

From what you can see, the cavern appears to be in a natural state, with no delicate carvings or engraved work. Sharp stone projects from the walls, and you suspect that the grotto has not been long torn from the fabric of the mountain. ***Turn to 398.***

"I am wary of passing this way," warns Bain.

"I say we continue." You try to convince the dwarf that this would be the best decision, but he remains skeptical. Guessing at the best line of advance, you start again, quickly becoming disoriented in the winding and sloping tunnels. Then the sound of scraping stone comes to you, though its direction is elusive.

"What is that?" you whisper to Bain who, has half-covered his crystal so that only a small pool of dim light bathes his feet and illuminates his features. There is a glimmer of uncertainty in his eye.

"To my ear, it is the sound of stone on stone, but moving of its own accord. We should retreat to those arched tunnels we left behind, but I am totally lost, and that I am ashamed to admit." Bain peers into the darkness from under his heavy eyebrows, but what he sees, if anything, you cannot guess.

"You lead, Bain," you say, again quietly. "In this dread darkness, you will be much more sure than I."

He replies, "I will lead, though I fear my guesses will be little better than yours."

After walking for a short time, doubling back through smaller tunnels at least twice, Bain mutters to you in a low voice. "To our left is a large cave, or so I would guess. Ahead lies this devilish tunnel. Which way to go?"

- *If you wish to enter the cave,* ***turn to 299.***
- *If you wish to continue along the tunnel,* ***turn to 391.***

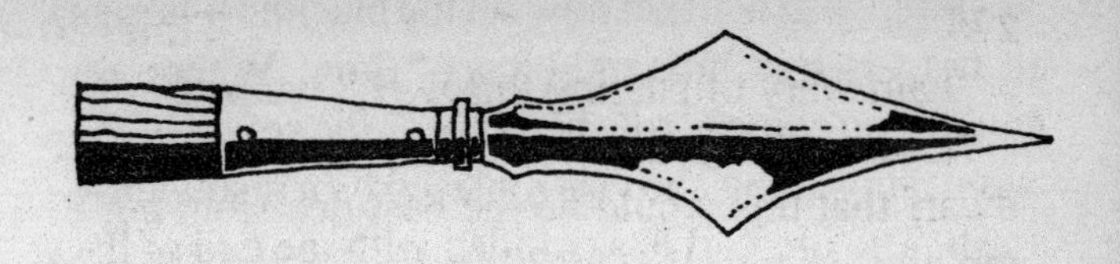

276 **Time: N/A**

"Though I know it is folly," says Bain, "I will stay with you while we explore this mine."

"Excellent!" you declare and bring your fist down upon the ore-laden cart to emphasize your triumph of reasoning: 'Thud!' "Now," you continue, as you walk down the dark corridor, "bring your light forward and we shall..." But as you speak, you hear a creaking and a grinding. "What is that?" you ask, more of yourself than your companion.

"The cart," says Bain frantically, "you have dislodged it."

You turn to look and see that it has begun to roll down the track. "Stop it!" you cry as both you and the dwarf spring to its side once more. But as Bain does so his foot is caught by the depression of the track and he trips forward, knocking his head against a metal buttress protruding from the front of the cart. He grunts and falls, dropping his crystal. It shatters and the light is doused. In the blackness, no word comes from Bain, though you hear the rolling of the cart close at hand. You grope ahead, and though you feel the side of it for a fleeting instant, it is quickly gone, gaining speed as it rolls down the tunnel.

[9]

"Bain," you whisper now for the blackness brings all horrors to mind, and close! "Bain! Where are you?" You come across his body as the sound of the cart rolling along ahead is replaced by a resounding crash. The ore-cart has collided with the end of the tunnel, or some barrier, and the sound does not soon die away. As you turn Bain's body over, a more ominous noise now comes. There is a rumbling and great cracking of stone. The vibrations of the cart's crash have loosened the rock overhead! Quickly, you lift Bain to your shoulder and begin to stumble back up the corridor, but it is too late. First small, then larger and larger boulders are dislodged from the ceiling. One of them gives you a nasty bump on the head, and you fall. Then, sadly, more and more rocks fall upon you, leaving you buried and painfully helpless. Your quest has come to a terrible and unforeseen conclusion. **The End.**

277 **Time: 0**

The ring fits perfectly! ***Pick a number*** *and add your Perception bonus:*

- *If 2-5,* ***turn to 332.***
- *If 6-12,* ***turn to 320.***

278 **Time: N/A**

Ever valiant, Bain fights to the end. Mercifully, you are quickly put to death, as the bloodthirsty goblins are anxious to see what is in your haversack. Your quest comes to a sad conclusion. **The End.**

279 **Time: 0**

"Kill it quickly," whispers Bain. You slap the spider off your hand, but not before it bites! In moments, your hand is swollen and aching. *Increase your Damage Taken by 20.*

- *If your Damage Taken now exceeds your Endurance,* ***turn to 396.***
- *Otherwise,* ***turn to 195.***

280 **Time: 0**

Bain appears just over the lip of the pit. With his help, you manage to pull yourself up and onto the solid floor of the corridor beyond. Like yours, Bain's breath is laboured. ***Turn to 330.***

281 **Time: 5**

"If we are to explore this way further, I think we should have a closer look at the pool first," you say. "There is something strange about it. Or maybe phantoms have the better of my mind."

"Then the same phantoms are in me," Bain admits. "I too find the pool disturbing — unnatural."

The two of you draw closer. At edge of the water, you peer in. ***Pick a number*** *and add your Perception bonus:*

- *If 2-7,* ***turn to 228.***
- *If 8-12,* ***turn to 243.***

282 **Time: 5**

The lockpick falls from your grasp! Now all you can do is watch on while your fate is decided. As the two arguing orcs begin to club one another, the leader laughs harshly. Vicious blows are exchanged and blood is drawn, but the battle lasts only a few moments. Soon one goblin lies in the dust on the stone floor.

The largest orc laughs again, a cruel guttural snort. Turning his attention to you and Bain, he barks a question at you in orc-speech, but you do not understand.

The big goblin snarls an order, and the other grabs the chains and jerks you to your feet. Much to everyone's surprise, the rusty chains break! Thinking quickly, Bain manages to snap his chains too. *Erase the Lockpick from your Character Record.* ***Pick a number*** *and add your General bonus:*

- *If 2-7,* ***turn to 293.***
- *If 8-12,* ***turn to 144.***

283 **Time: 20**

You walk down a dusty corridor which looks very much like many of the others. Shortly, you come to a clear icy spring, the water of which flows into a distinctive basin just before an archway leading to the next intersection of tunnels.

- *If you take a drink from the spring,* ***turn to 333.***
- *If you pass under the arch,* ***turn to 131.***

284 **Time: N/A**

"I know we will be late, but may good fortune smile upon us!" you say to Bain. ***Pick a number:***

- *If 2-5, **turn to 348.***
- *If 6-12, **turn to 319.***

285 **Time: N/A**

Overcome by the grip of several of the foul arms, you lose consciousness, just as the sensation of slipping beneath the cool black waters of the pool overcomes you. Your quest has come to a sad conclusion. **The End.**

286 **Time: 5**

As you and the dwarf move down the corridor, the sound of running water grows louder, and the unusual blue flowers cluster more thickly on the wall. The flowers have many little moths flying about them. After traveling a short way, you approach one of Moria's springwater chambers.

- *If you enter the room, **turn to 121.***
- *If you return back along the west passage, **turn to 328.***

287 **Time: 5**

Panic takes hold of you. There is a passage which opens up to your left just behind. “Do we fly or make our stand?” asks Bain urgently.

- *If you fight the troll that has appeared just ahead of you,* ***turn to 106.***
- *If you run and try to avoid the trolls,* ***pick a number*** *and add your General bonus:*
  - *If 2-9,* ***turn to 111.***
  - *If 10-12,* ***turn to 112.***

288 **Time: 5**

You run from the foul beast after hacking off one of its slimy arms. Bain does the same and follows close behind. When you come out of the cave and return to the intersection with the main corridor, you stop for a moment to catch your breath.

“That was a nasty surprise, and no mistake,” you say to the winded dwarf.

He answers, “I agree, and so I will not return that way. Even though this path dips down into water, I would wager that we will not find another one of those horrors yonder.”

Forced to traverse the main passage, you are soon on your way. ***Turn to 175.***

289 **Time: 0**

By some chance, both you and your companion manage a harrowing leap to safety—on the far side of the chasm! Behind you, the stone span plummets into depths unknown, far out of sight.

10

Once you catch your breath, you ask the dwarf if there might be another way out of the Great Hall, for there is obviously no returning this way.

"There might be," he answers, "but we will not discover it standing here." He makes his way over to the entrance of the Great Hall. ***Move on to B1*** *(The Great Hall).*

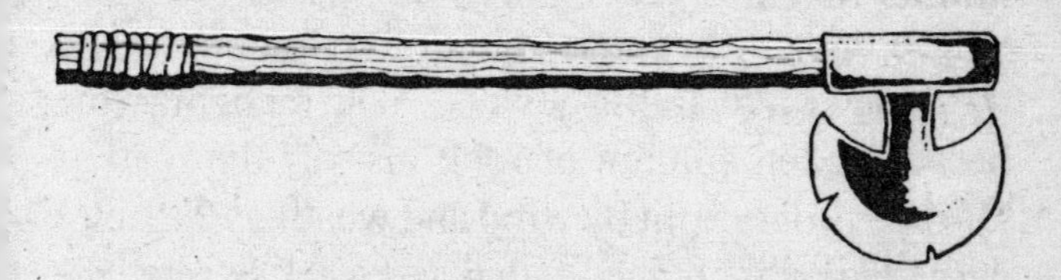

290 **Time: 60**

Hopelessly lost, you and the dwarf travel on guided only by the faint light of Bain's crystal. Then, after taking yet another confounded side-passage, a foul stench is brought to you upon the merest stirring of the air. "That smell is bad!" says Bain.

"No mistaking it though," you reply. "Carrion it is, and long dead I would say. The odour is mixed with others none better. It may be folly to seek it out. What say you?"

"I would no sooner come to its source than rot in some hole myself. I cannot make up my mind. You decide," urges your companion.

• *If you seek out the origin of the stench,* ***turn to 116.***
• *Otherwise,* ***turn to 303.***

Nearing the source of the Silverlode and the Falls, you pause with Bain to survey the impressive scene before you. The young dwarf appears dazed, overcome with emotion so near to Durin's Stone and Mirrormere, sacred sites of his race. Without a word, Bain dashes ahead, and you follow. You find him standing in a reverent pose beside the lake, whose dark, still waters reflect the mountains and the clouds like living jewels. You recognize the broad broken column of rock just off the road as Durin's Stone. Split by wind and weather, the runes carved upon it now too faded and weak to read, the stone retains a power that gives you as well as your companion pause. To your surprise, the dwarf begins to chant in a deep and sad voice.

"It is as I have heard in tales and song," says Bain excitedly after he has finished. "One can not see their reflection in Kheled-zâram, though the seven stars appear overhead. I must see Moria!"

"The Great Gates are but a short distance from here," you say. The broad but decrepit main road leads up to a niche in the mountainside above the Dale pierced by the Gates. You climb the wide stairway which leads to the oldest entrance into the mines of Moria. "I had heard these doors had been cast down some time ago, but here they seem remade, and of late." Bain does not comment but makes to enter the Black Pit while its doors stand ajar.

12

Following Bror's instructions and your own insatiable curiosity, you walk with a pounding heart past the Great Gates and enter the Mines of Moria.

Looking into Khazad-dûm for the first time, both you and the dwarf are struck speechless. It is difficult for any to fathom the complexity of the stronghold, yet just peering inside gives credence to what you have heard of Durin's concern for its defense.

A short walk leads to the Eastern Halls, the oldest chambers in all of Moria. The first you meet is the the Entry Hall, a large, square room with a high-peaked ceiling. You count fourteen narrow window shafts cut into the near and eastern wall, illuminating the room with an eerie and pale light.

Continuing down the wide passage for a quarter of a mile, you come to a broad stair leading down and then, to what was once Durin's Bridge, a slender arch of stone more that six man-heights across spanning what legend says is a bottomless abyss. All that remains of the once-splendid bridge are its shattered ends; tattered and broken outcroppings thrust into emptiness. In the gathering gloom, you can see that a crude rope bridge now extends across the chasm. "Probably the work of orcs," you whisper to Bain as you lead the way.

"Let us hope they have had little use for it recently." The dwarf follows.

7

Once over the bridge, you stop to examine the chamber you have entered: the Hall of Trees, named for the tree-shaped pillars supporting the high, curved ceiling. "We need a light!" you say. "I will be able to go no farther without one, even though you may be at home here." At this, Bain draws forth an amulet which he has until now kept concealed on a heavy chain under his tunic.

"A relic of older and better times," explains Bain. As he holds the crystal forth, it begins to emit a soft glimmer, then an ever-stronger light, until you can see the intricate tracings of stone overhead. But the light subsides, and soon a mere pool of it is cast upon the floor at your feet. "Neither of us needs fear the darkness of Moria," your companion says. "The dwarf-craft of my Fathers will see us through. Now for the Chamber of Records, or Mazarbul as we dwarves would call it." Bain seems changed, now within the halls of the Black Pit. He is stronger and more confident; not the same fellow who would have had you steal your way through Lórien!

To your right is a passage. "That is the way," says Bain.

- *If you enter the passage to the Chamber of Records,* ***turn to 155.***
- *If you first wish to explore the Deeps of Moria,* ***turn to 203.***

Soon, the tunnel branches. Consulting Bror's map, you feel certain of where you are.

This intersection is more elaborate than most. Two elongated dwarf-heads carved from red stone stand on each side of the corridor where it divides. The huge, empty eyes of the statues seem half-asleep; what they have seen, you can only guess at.

The archways for the corridors ahead are decorated with tree-crowned columns of black marble. However, a third and smaller corridor, not on your map, leads off to the left. For this side tunnel, the stonework is fair, but no elaborate decorations mark its walls.

"Well," says Bain, "it seems to me quite clear that we should take the main passage to the left."

"So it would seem," you answer. But as you make ready to go that way, you catch a glimpse of movement in the deadly blackness far down that path. "What is that?" you ask Bain, whispering. "Your eyes are better than mine in the dark."

"Indeed they are, my friend, and if they have true sight, I would say they just saw a dwarf — no, two dwarves running ahead of us!"

"Dwarves!" you exclaim.

"My uncle's cousins have come before us," says your companion, cursing under his breath.

"They could not be remnants of Balin's expedition all those years ago?"

"I doubt that very much," says Bain. "I have heard that they were slain to the last in the Chamber of Mazarbul. And if they were Balin's folk, why would they run ahead of us as we approached? No, I say they are agents meant to prevent our getting the Will to Bror."

You look once again down the left branch of the main corridor. "Bror's cousins, or their agents await our next move. But we know not their number nor the fate they would bestow upon us. Could they find the Will of Old Bror by themselves?"

"No. Its location is a secret I alone carry. That is why they have not assailed us yet. They want us to find the Will first. What should we do?" Bain sounds despondent. The nearness of hostile dwarves seems to unsettle him.

"We should not stay here, that much is clear." With that said, you make your decision.

- *If you follow the dwarves down the left branch of the main corridor,* ***turn to 274.***
- *If you take the right branch of the main corridor,* ***turn to 325.***
- *If you explore the smaller, unmarked corridor,* ***turn to 102.***

293 **Time: N/A**

The angry orcs catch you, nearly crushing you in their claws. The larger one grunts and raises his club; Bain is nowhere to be seen. Your quest ends here, with you falling prey to the fearsome Goblins of Moria. **The End.**

[8]

294 **Time: 10**

After walking further, you and Bain approach a series of arches bracing the corridor's walls. ***Turn to 342.***

295 **Time: N/A**

Your hold on the edge of the bridge is too weak, and despite your desperate efforts and Bain's attempt to reach you, your fingers lose their grip! You quest ends here, in an endless fall into the Deeps of Moria. **The End.**

296 **Time: 0**

You leap out of the crack onto the ledge beyond just behind Bain, turn left, and then run along the ledge with arrows following. You look back to see a group of armoured goblins, numbering twenty or more, rushing along the pathway also. Some of them carry torches, newly lit, while all of them raise a battle cry and pursue you.

With longer strides, you pass the dwarf — though that is dangerous — and hold the crystal ahead of you. "Hurry!" you urge. "Doom follows us!" ***Turn to 197.***

4

297 **Time: 0** **Exp Pt: 45**

The fight is bloody, and the dwarves ask no quarter. You are forced to slay your opponent as Bain takes his.

When the deeds are done and the two agents lay still at your feet, you ask Bain who they were.

"As we had suspected, they were Bror's cousins. They must have left the camp shortly after we, then come to Moria before us. But this is a sad day — as it should be when dwarf is forced to kill dwarf. There are precious few of us left in the world as it is."

"This is behind us now," you say. "We must find the Will before we can say our work is done." Bain takes a last look at his dead kinsmen, then sets off about the chamber once more in search of the treasure vault. ***Move on** to any "B" Location.*

298 **Time: 0**

Heaving open the chest's lid, you glance in to determine its contents. Besides some greaves and pieces of leather armour fitted for a dwarf, you spy a fine prize. There lays a recurved bow of white wood and three gleaming arrows with hard steel tips. All these you snatch up.

Note that the arrows, when fired from the bow, add a +2 bonus to your Missile OB. Once fired, these arrows are lost forever. Add the bow and arrows set to your Character Record if you wish to play this character in another Middle-earth Quest book. ***Turn to 301.***

11

"Through the cave I say, and quickly!" you urge. "I feel some doom coming upon us."

"I feel it too," says Bain as he enters the wide cavern. There are tiers, like steps, which lead to its floor. You begin to cross, when the ominous sound returns, now louder than before. "It is a shuffling, or shambling," and you can only agree with the dwarf. The sound is like stone rumbling against the stone of hard ground; it echoes all around you.

Unnerved, Bain raises his amulet and from it bursts forth a blinding radiance. The high cave is revealed for an instant, and you see that many cracks appear in its walls, leading to other tunnels and grottoes no doubt. But as the crystal dims once more, you catch a glimpse of light reflected off of dead black eyes peering out of one of the fissures.

"Bain!" you restrain a hoarse cry. "Did you see them?"

"Those, and others." Your companion's voice is grim and hollow, like the deathly space around you. "Ready your weapon, though I fear it will be of little use. We are surrounded by cave-trolls, and their skin is stone — hard armour for mere steel."

Just as Bain raises his axe, there is a mighty howl which booms through the cave. It is answered by others on the far side, and the tumult which they raise is enough to turn your legs to limp seaweed, and your sword arm to rope.

9

"Steady," says Bain. "We must make for one of the fissures that harbour no trolls." Then; "Run! They are here!"

Huge black shapes move out of the darkness, and they are fast! From a fleeting, sidelong glance you see a frightening visage of pale, black eyes and gaping maw full with teeth. A hammer or stone club swings down and crashes into the floor where you had just stood not a moment before; splinters of rock fly up to strike you, but you have already started running with Bain, who has his faint crystal held before him. "Follow me!" he cries. ***Pick a number*** *and add your Running bonus:*

- *If 2-10,* ***turn to 108.***
- *If 11-12,* ***turn to 109.***

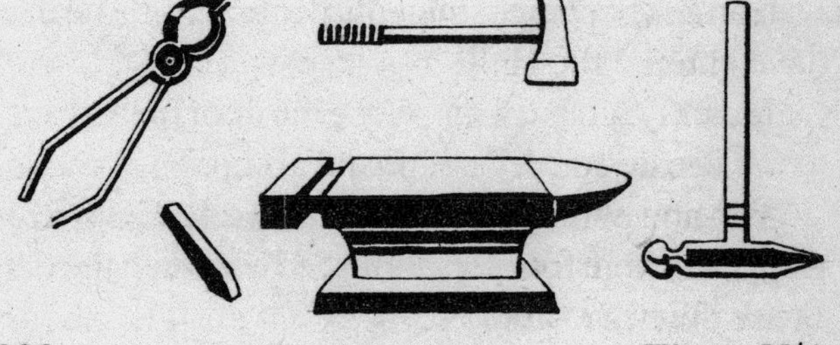

300 **Time: N/A**

As the powerful cave snake crushes you, the dwarf is unable to help. Gasping "Bain..." you lose consciousness. Your ill-fated quest comes to a sad conclusion. **The End.**

'Thrum, thrum!' beat the orc-drums; they sound closer.

"The Will!" cries Bain. You see him standing at one of the chamber's pillars, in front of a compartment now revealed. You run over and inspect the hollow niche that Bain has somehow discovered and opened, then take the rolled parchment from his hands. Unfurling it, you see that the paper is covered with inked runes. Although you cannot immediately determine what they say, in the bottom corner you find the rune of Old Bror, the same one inscribed on the rune-key.

"It is the Will — there is no mistake," you say anxiously. "But are we too late to get it out of Moria?" As you speak, the 'thrum thrum' of the war-drums becomes suddenly deafening. "The orcs have entered the Hall!"

"Quickly, go back and close the door to the vault, or we are doomed!" commands Bain.

"But how will we get out?" you wail. "We will be trapped in here forever, or flushed out when the orcs break down the door."

"I said close the door! I will find a safe route out." Bain holds up the rune-key with a wry smile breaking over his lips. Then you bound down the low tunnel and shut the door tight just as orcish arrows are shot toward you.

As you pass back down to the vault, you can hear the first hammerings on the door behind and the tireless 'thrum, thrum!' of the goblin-drums.

5

"That door, however well-made, will not stand the assault of all those orcs for long," you say desperately to Bain, but he is busy searching the far wall of the chamber. "What are you looking for?"

"Our way out. If you would be quiet for a moment, perhaps I could find it!"

You turn back once more and hear the stone of Bram's door crack. "They will be here soon..."

"That has done it!" calls the dwarf back to you. "Come hither." You run up to Bain, who has found yet another concealed door. "Ha ha! Leave it to dwarves when you are in a tight spot," he chortles.

Passing through into the chamber beyond, you close the door just in time to hear the other one battered in. ***Turn to 389.***

7

302 **Time: 5**

You and the dwarf desperately need air, but the tunnel remains under water. You turn around, hoping that you have not come too far and will be able to get back. Not a moment before the water claims you, first the dwarf, then you burst back into the main passage.

"As I suspected, we will find nothing that way," says a weary, wet Bain.

"Then onwards," you gasp, cursing your decision to try the watery passage. ***Turn to 134.***

303 **Time: Several Days**

Unfortunately, you and Bain have become eternally lost within the Deeps of Moria and no amount of back-tracking and searching will show you the way back out again. Hunger and darkness take your life. Your quest has come to a sad conclusion. **The End.**

304 **Time: N/A**

You look up to see a small, stocky dwarf standing before you. His beard is shorter and not so thick as Bror's. In the starlight his face, while set in a fierce demeanour, has an air of wonder and youthful curiosity about it. You introduce yourself.

The young dwarf nods. He carries an axe in his belt and a bow over one shoulder. Both weapons are ornately decorated, and obviously of fine dwarf-make.

"I am Bain," says the dwarf, "and am pleased to meet you, if we can indeed recover Old Bror's Will."

"That we can do, but first we must get away from this camp and your uncle's cousins. We have but fourteen days."

After sleeping near the banks of the Celebrant, you set out together the next morning for the East Gate of Moria. It is mid-autumn, and the weather is cool but sunny.

A day of travel along the grassy, serpentine Elven path south of the swift-running Celebrant brings you and the dwarf to a bridge. ***Turn to 339.***

305 **Time: 10**

The chest is locked, and you have no key. *You must try to pick the lock.* ***Pick a number*** *and add your Trickery bonus:*

- *If 2-7,* ***turn to 166.***
- *If 8-12,* ***turn to 214.***

306 **Time: 0**

Unfortunately, you find nothing within the box.

"I must insist that we leave here and make our way to the Great Hall as quickly as possible," says an indignant Bain.

"We will come there," you reply, "when I am ready, and not before."

A darkening shadow draws over the dwarf. ***Turn to 307.***

307 **Time: 0**

The shelves behind the standing doors hold several items of interest. You see a small metal box, a large green wooden box, and a stack of papers. *You may examine each item only once.*

- *If you open the small metal box,* ***turn to 191.***
- *If you open the large wooden box,* ***turn to 306.***
- *If you examine the papers,* ***turn to 410.***
- *Otherwise,* ***turn to 195.***

308 **Time: 0** **Exp Pt: 2**

You have made it across! With a tumble, Bain lands just behind you. You catch your breath and eye the dark pit. ***Turn to 330.***

309 **Time: 0**

Bain notices a tattered piece of stained parchment lying within the dislodged coal.

You easily free the paper, which appears to be an engineering drawing for a large bridge with a trap. A great winch and cog- driven steel pivot mechanism anchors the span and allows it to rotate laterally, permitting the bridge to be rolled into a spanned chasm in time of crisis. You suspect that some dwarf- engineer hid the plans during the last attack before Moria was overrun and became the exclusive domain of the Balrog.

If you keep the Bridge Plan, add it to your Character Record. ***Move on*** *to any "A" Location.*

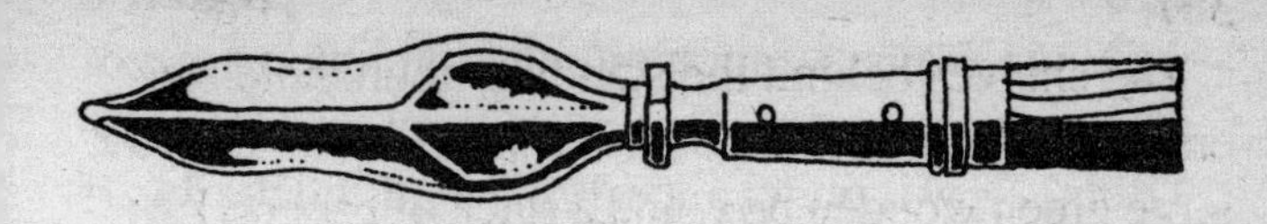

310 **Time: 0**

The ring does not fit, regardless of which finger you try to place it on. Though you consider leaving it here, you realize that you may be able to sell it after your quest is completed. *If you keep the Ring, add it to your Character Record.* ***Move on*** *to any "A" Location.*

311 **Time: N/A**

Perspiring and out of breath, you find shade under an elm at the riverside and anxiously await the return of Bain. Time passes slowly. Then, without a word, two tall elves deposit a shaken Bain at your feet and depart.

In response to your questions, Bain refuses to offer an explanation of his behaviour. ***Turn to 251.***

312 **Time: 10**

"Bain, this way is clear. Follow me!"

The dwarf dodges his foes, and though sorely wounded, he follows. You take a passage off to one side and proceed down ever narrowing tunnels, avoiding stone axes and rocks hurled through the darkness. Eventually, the noise of pursuit dies off until you can hear no more. ***Turn to 184.***

313 **Time: 30**

Driving your weapon into the unblinking eye of the spider, you cause it to back away momentarily. "Bain! Now is our chance. Fly!" You and the dwarf run up one tunnel, then down another, trying to get further and further from the spider and its wicked lair. After you have run out of breath, you ask Bain to stop since he is ahead of you. "A moment," you plead.

"We may have more than a moment, and several more on top of that," says the dwarf gravely. "We are lost, and I have no idea how to find our way again." ***Turn to 303.***

314 **Time: N/A**

Bain is relentless and as stubborn as any of Durin's Folk. Concluding that you may sooner change the mind of an Ent, you are forced to follow the young dwarf along the grassy banks of the river. Sure-footed and quick, Bain is not as quiet as you might like.

Within a few minutes, you feel as though you are being carefully observed. Bain appears unconcerned, perhaps eager to confront the elves of Lórien. Then, just ahead, you meet an elf astride the path. His grey eyes search yours and quickly dismiss you and the dwarf as figures of little import. Dressed in a forest-grey tunic and carrying a bow over his shoulder, the elf raises a hand. In Westron, he says: "In the name of the Lady of Lórien, I command you to return whence you came. Immediately!"

9

Beside you, Bain bristles, fingering his axe. "Do not be a fool," you whisper. To the elf, you add: "We shall do as you ask." Bowing, you drag the dwarf with you. Once out of sight of the Wood-elf, you lose your temper with Bain. "I am leading this expedition, dwarf! Do as I say or I'll leave you tied to an oak."

"You fear the elf. I do not. This is the path we must take," Bain argues, looking back.

"Do you think he was alone? I would wager a pair of archers were waiting for you to draw forth that axe of yours. Come with me now or return to your uncle alone. You have no other choice."

Instead of following you to the rope bridge, Bain leaves the path, plunging deeper into the woods. Once again, you are forced to follow him, but soon a strange sensation overtakes you. The air grows heavy. A wind arises, resisting your incursion. When the dwarf pauses at a broad path leading north and deeper into Lórien, you grab his arm.

"Dwarf, I'm weary of this sport," you whisper harshly, certain that the elves will send an arrow through your throat at any moment. "You risk our lives. I would rather that we were south of the Celebrant marching all day and all night to make time."

"I will stay here until nightfall," says Bain, "then take the path west to Kheled-zâram."

Weary of argument, you realize that the dwarf cares not for the elven-kind — he is young and foolish. Is it your duty to stay with him? "You dishonour your family and your race," you snap. ***Pick a number*** *and add your Perception bonus:*

- *If 2-9,* ***turn to 324.***
- *If 10-12,* ***turn to 143.***

315 **Time: N/A**

You have just crouched down under an elm to await the dwarf when he scurries over the bridge, obviously relieved that you waited for him.

"Came to your senses, did you?" you ask Bain. "Or did the elves help you?"

Bain lowers his gaze and begins to walk along the path south of the Celebrant. ***Turn to 251.***

316 **Time: 5**

The fissure is a great crack which rises far up the wall of the cave. The inky blackness of its foldings is not easily pushed back by the dwarf-crystal. "Who should enter first?" asks Bain.

A fair question, to be sure. The way is narrow; that is as much as you can tell. It may be best to send your companion ahead, for he is somewhat slighter than you and may be able to find the way easier. "Well?" Bain persists.

- *If you enter the fissure first,* ***turn to 188.***
- *If you send Bain in first,* ***turn to 192.***

317 **Time: 0**

You make an extraordinary effort as you fall and are just able to grasp a solid edge at the far end of the bridge! There, just a few feet away, Bain too hangs by a precarious hold. ***Pick a number*** *and add your General bonus:*

- *If 2-5,* ***turn to 295.***
- *If 6-12,* ***turn to 326.***

318 **Time: 10**

As you walk along, the corridor turns, and you can no longer see the Watcher-statue. There is more dust here, some of it floating in the air. Along the top of the tunnel, light-stones flicker to life as you approach; you are able to see clearly.

After a short span of time, you come to another junction. By now, you realize that the map which Bror gave you is very much out of date and that many new tunnels have been delved since it was drawn. The corridor you travel enters the junction through an archway decorated with onyx-inlaid runes. ***Turn to 120.***

319 **Time: N/A**

Bror and the dwarven party anxiously await your arrival at the familiar camp-site. Before you have time to explain your tardiness, Bror snatches the Will from your hand, reading it voraciously.

"This is the Will!" he proclaims to a round of cheers from his companions — the greedy cousins are conspicuously absent. "Let us be off!" Bain joins him, and the dwarves hastily pack their belongings.

"But what of the other fine things I brought back from Moria?" you ask, eager to make a profit from your travails. You shake the bag holding the valuables you gathered in the fabled dwarven kingdom.

Bror glares at you. "You return late, jeopardizing our endeavour, and expect us to heed your desires.

Farewell, adventurer! Seek your fortune elsewhere!"

Left literally holding the bag, you watch in anguish as the dwarves leave the riverside to return to their home, Will in hand. You grit your teeth and settle down for the night, already planning where you will go to sell thc goods, and what journey you might undertake next. No matter what the dwarf said, you were successful in your quest, just a little late. After all, few have ventured into Moria, and fewer yet have returned.

The night falls with a bright shroud of stars, each holding the promise of another quest, another day. **The End.**

320 **Time: 0**

This artifact will be useful! *While wearing the ring, you may add 1 to your Perception bonus and 1 to your Trickery bonus. However, the ring will not work if you wear another magic ring at the same time.* ***Move on*** *to any "A" Location.*

321 **Time: 5**

Considering the importance of what lies beyond and the suspected presence of unfriendly agents, you and the dwarf decide that the bridge must hide a deadly trap. However, you are unable to find a mechanism anywhere. ***Pick a number*** *and add your Perception bonus:*

- *If 2-8,* ***turn to 404.***
- *If 9-12,* ***turn to 267.***

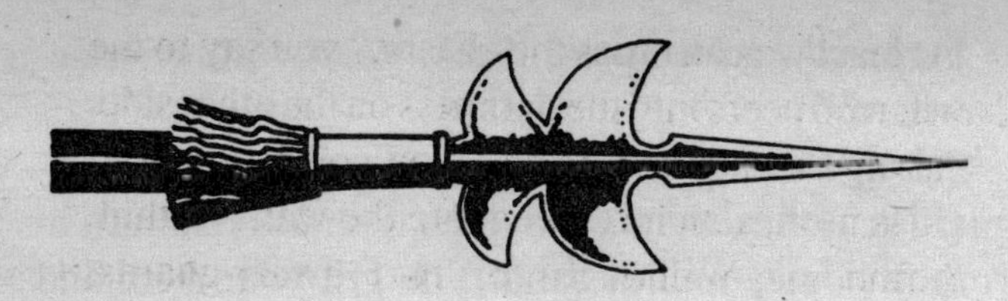

322 **Time: 0**

You leave the crack behind, but from around the bend in the path behind come a group of armoured goblins, numbering twenty or more, some carrying torches. When they see the two of you on the ledge they raise a battle cry and rush with scimitars bared.

"We cannot prevail against such numbers!" says Bain at your side, "Quickly, this way!" He bounds off along the pathway. With longer strides, you pass the dwarf — though that is dangerous — and hold the crystal ahead of you. ***Turn to 197.***

323 **Time: 10**

You and Bain soon stand at another bridged chasm.

"Let us consult Bror's map once more," requests Bain.

Once you have it out, Bain remarks that this is probably the second crevasse indicated, and that the two of you are following the correct path. Interestingly, it is quite evident that the bridge harbours a trap mechanism, now rendered useless. Nearby, you see that a huge piece of jagged metal has been forced through an inconspicuous crack at the base of the bridge.

"At least we can cross the chasm," you say to the dwarf, who peers into the darkness on the other side.

Having crossed the bridge, you come to an old guard station, a niche carved into the wall. Within, you find room enough for two dwarf-guards, though it is empty, of course.

Passing by, you walk down the quiet passage as random light-stones illuminate your way. For about a quarter of a mile, the corridor gently slopes down to the south-east. ***Turn to 264.***

324 **Time: N/A**

Crouched on his heels and still as stone, Bain resists you. "I would lie in the Halls of my Fathers before I would yield to an elf!" he vows. You think he will come to his senses, lest elven arrows test his armour. Shadows deepen; the Golden Wood grows dark.

- *If you go back to the bridge,* ***turn to 271.***
- *If you stay with Bain,* ***turn to 182.***

325 **Time: 10**

Having taken the passage to the right, you and the dwarf soon find yourselves unwittingly entering a long, dark cavern. No luminous mosses or light-stones push back the hollow and immense black-ness of the grotto.

"Give us your light, Bain. Let us see what we can find in this great cave."

"Speak quietly," whispers the dwarf. "I fear it may already be too late." Then, from ahead, you hear the patter of unshod feet. ***Pick a number*** *and add your Perception bonus:*

- *If 2-7,* ***turn to 125.***
- *If 8-12,* ***turn to 255.***

326 **Time: 10** **Exp Pt: 10**

Your hold on the edge of the bridge is just strong enough to allow you to pull yourself, and then Bain, back up. As you lie next to the moving bridge you realize that it shows no sign of ceasing its wrench-ing pitch. On hands and knees, you crawl to the corridor leading away from the chasm.

6

As you look back, you see the entire span slowly twist upside-down and fall into the deep pit with a crash. The bridge is gone. ***Pick a number:***

- *If 2-5,* ***turn to 151.***
- *If 6-12,* ***turn to 141.***

327 **Time: 10**

Soon after taking the left path, the ceiling gently lowers down to a mere and restricting height of four feet. Both you and the dwarf are forced to bend over to proceed.

Within moments, you come upon a low door, no more than three feet in height. It is peaked and gird with deeply engraved runes after the dwarvish fashion. Bain moves up next to it, and holding his crystal up to the writing, begins to read. "It says — 'Here lies Noin, son of Narni. Know that he lived long, graced by Durin, and made fine crafts of armour.'"

"The tomb of an armourer," you repeat with somewhat less reverence. It is well-known that dwarves bury their dead with their most prized possessions.

- *If you wish to enter the tomb,* ***turn to 334.***
- *If you pass by the tomb and continue on,* ***turn to 352.***

328 **Time: 10**

After crossing the bridge and crawling past the boulder, you and the dwarf return to the junction of several passages. ***Turn to 211.***

329 **Time: 15**

You awaken bloody and weak. Due to Bain's valiant efforts, the bats were driven off. Unsteadily, you regain your feet and begin to follow the dwarf to the cave entrance. "Hurry," says Bain, "they will soon be upon us again." ***Turn to 138.***

330 **Time: 10**

You look back up the stairs, expecting to be pursued, but the wide, shallow steps are empty. However, gathered at the top is a group of bent orcs, howling and cursing in their harsh tongue. You motion Bain to follow, but he lingers, eyeing the orcs as if to challenge them. "Why do they not pursue?" he asks. "They have the advantage."

"I am grateful they do not. But you can be certain they are frightened of something down here; we have ignorance on our side. Let us be off and hope we fare well." At that you turn and walk forward.

A little way down the passage, Bain solemnly pulls out the amulet. Almost immediately, small hidden stones set deeply in the walls glow in reply. You can see the corridor clearly now and wonder: what magic this is! The walls are smooth, and the heavy dust upon the floor rises in small clouds in the wake of your steps. Yet the air is fresh. The ages-old ventilation system of Durin's Folk still works! The foul orc-smell disappears for the moment, replaced by a faintly musty odour that is not entirely unpleasant. You feel more confident, moving softly so that your footsteps — like the silent dwarf's — do not echo away before you. ***Turn to 145.*** 8

331 **Time: 5**

Looking closely at the workbench, you see the outline of a secret drawer and manage to pry it open. Inside you discover a small sack containing a wooden doll no larger than your open hand and carved in the likeness of a mannish child. The doll is dressed after the fashion of Gondor many ages past. Bain reminds you that some dwarves excelled at making cunning toys. Doubtless, this doll was meant to be sold in Gondor. *If you keep the Doll, enter it on your Character Record.* ***Move on*** *to any "A" Location.*

332 **Time: 0**

The ring seems to have an enchanted nature, but you have no notion of what it does — if anything.

Bain becomes uninterested in the band and you are left with it. *If you keep the ring, add it to your Character Record.* ***Move on*** *to any "A" Location.*

333 **Time: 0**

As you bend down to the basin to take a cool draught, Bain grabs your shoulder. "Do not drink of it!" he warns, quite concerned. "As I said before, while Moria is held under the sway of orcs, all is unclean. The mountain, and all within it, including the waters, rebel."

- *If you think Bain is crazed and so take a drink,* ***turn to 177.***
- *If you turn aside from the water and pass under the arch to the next intersection,* ***turn to 131.***

You raise a hand to push open the door, but quick as lightning, Bain grabs your hand in a fierce grip that is, at best, over-tight. "What are you doing?" you ask, rather shocked.

The dwarf's crystal, which now hangs about his neck, casts strange and wavering shadows over his face, but the fire in his eyes is clear and piercing. "You shall not enter," he states plainly.

"I will do as I choose. Who are you to stop me?"

"I am a dwarf! And I will not stand by and allow a tomb occupied by another of my kind to be rummaged through just so that odd trinkets and other things which strike your fancy can be carried off. Find an orc-hole if that is what pleases you, though I would think those foul spawn do not revere their dead."

- *If you insist upon entering,* ***turn to 337.***
- *If you pass the tomb by and continue along the corridor,* ***turn to 356.***

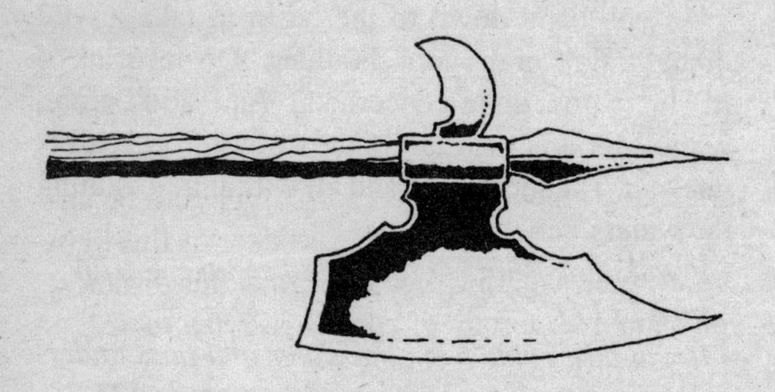

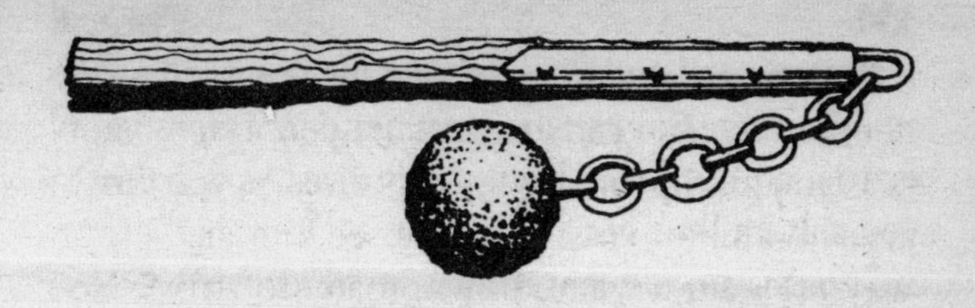

335 **Time: 5**

You break away from the orcs, and pulling Bain along, make for the entrance of the cave. "We must get away!" you yell, but the dwarf is too concerned with flight to respond. Soon you return to the intersection where the main corridor branches right and left. Although the sounds of pursuit strangely die behind you, there is little time to make a considered decision. The orcs could be upon you at any moment!

- *If you take the left branch of the main corridor,* ***turn to 274.***
- *If you take the unmarked side tunnel,* ***turn to 102.***

336 **Time: 0**

Across the dark chasm you can just discern some movement along what you would guess to be another walking-ledge. A hidden flicker of fire-light shows some skulking creature, but at this distance, you cannot be certain of what it is. ***Turn to 411.***

5

337 **Time: 0**

Pushing the dwarf away, you place a hand on the door, and make ready to push it open. Bain simply tells you to stop, but his voice is dire. As you turn to argue with him yet again, you see him just a short way off with his axe drawn, ready to strike. You consider the situation for a moment, then back down. "Perhaps I was impudent," you say to calm the dwarf. "You are right, of course. It would be wrong to disturb the peace of your forefathers. Forgive me." Bain lowers his weapon and the fire dies within him.

"We will not enter," he says, putting the incident to rest and leading you down the low corridor. ***Turn to 356.***

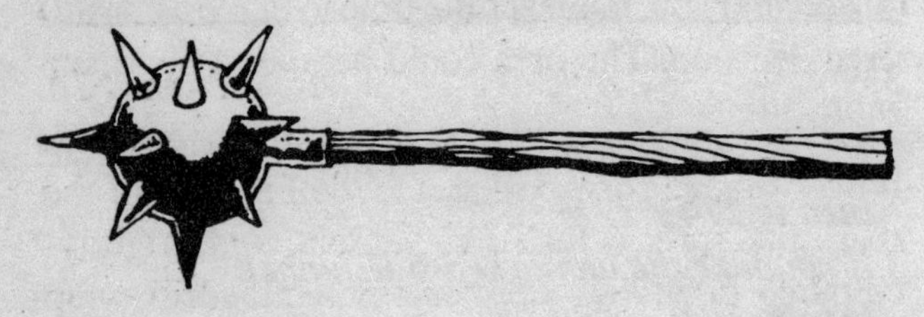

338 **Time: 0**

You open the lid of the small coffer and within find a handful of marvelous jewels. There are five emeralds, three rubies and deep blue sapphire.

Note that the emeralds are worth five gold coins each, the rubies are worth ten gold coins each, and the sapphire is worth thirty gold coins. Add these gems to your Character Record if you wish to play this character in another Middle-earth Quest gamebook. ***Turn to 301.***

6

339 **Time: N/A**

Across the blue water stretches an elegant, flower-draped rope bridge. On the far bank of the river, the grass is lush and verdant, and brightly-coloured flowering vines and grape tendrils wrap themselves around trees like decorations. A bird hidden somewhere in the branches of a mallorn sings a sprightly melody.

"The work of elves," you comment, admiring the craftsmanship of the bridge. Bain says nothing. Adjusting your haversack, you march on. When you notice that the dwarf is no longer nearby, you turn. There stands Bain, poised in thoughtful silence at the first rung of the rope bridge.

9

"Bain, hold! Our path does not lie that way. Beyond is the realm of the Golden Lady, and from what I have heard, she does not suffer trespassers lightly. Please, let us continue this way." You motion for the dwarf to follow.

Bain folds his arms, glaring at the bridge as though it offered some great challenge. "I believe we can travel to Dimrill Dale faster if we pass unnoticed by way of the girding of Lórien," he says flatly. "If my uncle's cousins or their agents know of our mission, they will try to get to Khazad-dûm before us. We may prevent that by taking a path on the other side of the Celebrant."

"Dwarf, have you been taken by some madness? We would both be full of elf-arrows before a day's travel was out. We cannot go that way. Bror would be most upset." You continue reasoning with the dwarf, but he has already taken the first tentative steps to cross the bridge.

He will not be stopped! Thinking that your sponsor might withhold the promised reward if you return alone, you are forced to follow Bain. Once on the far bank of the Celebrant, you argue vehemently with him, but he seems undeterred. ***Pick a number and add your Perception bonus:***

- *If 2-8, **turn to 314.***
- *If 9-12, **turn to 143.***

340 **Time: 0**

You and the dwarf breathe deeply of the dank tunnel air before entering the submerged, smaller passage. Bending over, the two of you are soon under water and moving as quickly as you can. ***Pick a number*** *and add your General bonus:*

- *If 2-7,* ***turn to 178.***
- *If 8-12,* ***turn to 302.***

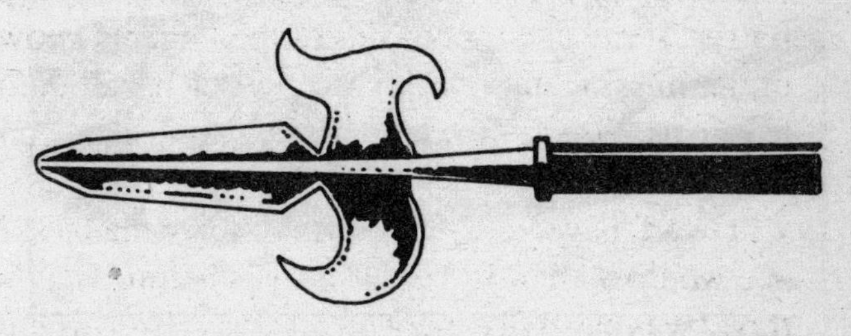

341 **Time: 5**

The drawer contains six parchment sheets, letters written in the script of ancient dwarf-runes. Bain takes them and begins reading. Shortly, he says, "This is not the Will. I doubt that it is to be found within this chamber. Let us be off!" With that, Bain tucks the letters inside his tunic.

"If that is not the Will, why keep the papers?" you ask.

"They are notes prepared by the master of this foundry. I think my uncle might find some use in them, if only to learn more about those who came before." With that, Bain has finished speaking of the papers. ***Turn to 195.***

342 **Time: 5**

Passing under archways decorated with typically well-constructed, axe-head stonework which has withstood centuries of neglect, you enter a corridor illuminated by small, hidden light-stones.

After rounding a gentle curve, you come upon another upturned and smashed Watcher-in-Stone, this one carved from onyx. The Watcher once took the form of a great bird, its wings outstretched as if ready to take flight. You find small pieces of the bird's onyx feathers, but the eyes — probably once set with beryls as Bain notes — are empty.

You do not spend much time examining the Watcher, because you have reached yet another branching of corridors. This time, three tunnels extend before you. ***Turn to 211.***

343 **Time: 15**

After passing under the arch, you walk on for some distance along a gently curving and smooth-walled tunnel. Beyond a crystal-veined archway, you come to another corridor junction.
Turn to 131.

344 **Time: 0**

The bridge you now approach spans a considerable gulf; the rockwork around it is natural and rugged. ***Pick a number*** *and add your Perception bonus:*

- *If 2-8,* ***turn to 321.***
- *If 9-12,* ***turn to 267.***

345 **Time: 5**

The room beyond the door is in a terrible way. Someone has set fire to the rug and pieces of wooden furniture in the centre of the room. Soot hangs heavily from the ceiling and walls. Off to one side, a table has been beaten into splinters, and the remnants of chairs can be seen. In the air, a faint odour of orcs lingers menacingly.

"There is nothing here for us," says Bain. In agreement, the two of you leave and return to the last corridor intersection. ***Turn to 120.***

346 **Time: 25**

Though it takes some time to convince you, Bain insists that the two of you are now far to the west of the map's main passage (which you have been hoping to find). His arguments are ultimately convincing, and the two of you return the way you had come. *Note that you may not again explore the Cart Track tunnel.* ***Turn to 378.***

347 **Time: 120**

You and Bain walk for almost a mile up a twisting passageway, climbing six more sets of stairs. When you reach what should be the Chamber of Mazarbul on the seventh level of the old city, a huge pile of rubble greets you; the rocks are blackened, as if subjected in the past to a great display of power and heat. Tired and discouraged, you and the dwarf retrace your steps to the winding passageway leading to Bror's family tunnels. ***Turn to 198.***

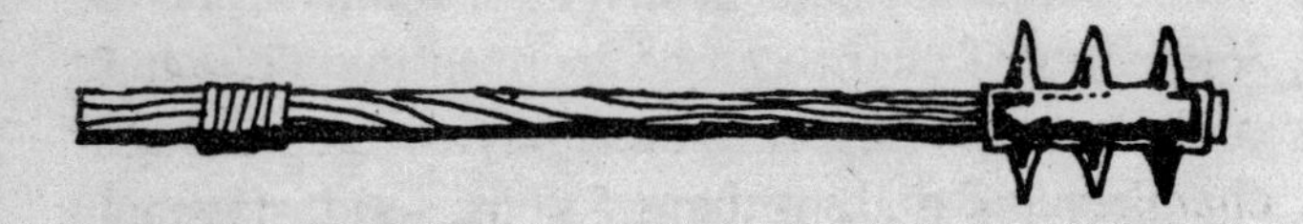

348 **Time: N/A**

You return with Bain to the camp-site to find it abandoned. Your heart sinks like a stone tossed into Moria's deepest pit.

"Fool! Malingerer!" Bain snaps, swatting at you with his hood. "We're too late! The Will is useless now, and my family disgraced and ruined!"

You allow the enraged dwarf to abuse and taunt you, knowing in your heart that he is right. Finding the Will in Moria and emerging with it was only part of your quest. Returning with it to the camp-site by the agreed-upon date was also part of the deal, and such speed proved to be more than you could manage. You have failed.

Bain will not acknowledge your pleas for mercy until tiring himself. He soundly curses you, then disappears into the trees along the riverside.

Alone, you make camp, nursing a whipped spirit and a weary body. 'Yet,' you vow, 'there shall be other adventures!' The night falls like a shroud, and a thousand stars light the sky, each holding the promise of another quest, another day. **The End.**

349 **Time: 5** **Exp Pt: 4**

You successfully traverse the trapped area and continue down the corridor without further difficulty. ***Turn to 292.***

350 **Time: 5**

The room, which once must have been a storage chamber, is dark as pitch and holds fetid, stagnant air. Rotting mats cover the floor. "This place has sheltered orcs recently," warns Bain. "Though I am not sure that any are close by now."

- *If you wish to explore the room further,* ***turn to 123.***
- *If you continue to travel up the corridor,* ***turn to 323.***

351 **Time: 20**

"You are right, Bain," you say to the dwarf. "There is nothing for us down this way. Let us return and try to find the right path to the Great Hall of your family." You both then turn and make the long journey back to the last intersection of tunnels and decorated archways. *Note that you may not again explore the Cart Track tunnel.* ***Turn to 378.***

---

352 **Time: 5**

The two of you walk on until you enter a small chamber from which several tunnels lead away. "A fine choice we have now," you say with a heavy heart.

"It may be easier than you suspect," begins Bain. "Do you feel the draft?"

"Yes," you answer, for a cool breeze blows across your face.

"It comes from that way." You companion leads you over to a tunnel opposite. It leads upward. Unlike the others, you can see that it soon opens out into a wider chamber. The other passageways lead down or twist quickly out of sight, and they are black.

"Very well, we shall go that way, but I feel myself getting ever more lost and desperate."

"We have little hope of getting back the way we came," reminds the dwarf, "unless we can sprout wings and fly back up that shaft."

"Yes. Now I am truly sorry that we came this way after all. How can we ever hope to get to the Great Hall?" You are despondent and worried that you may not be able to find your way back out to meet Bror. Not that you would want to with empty hands.

The two of you walk up the tunnel. ***Turn to 359.***

353 **Time: 0** **Exp Pt: 10**

With drawn string, Bain lets fly one of his own shafts and with it knocks a climbing goblin back into the rift. The 'thrum-thrum' of the orc-drums drive on the others though and they have come close to the edge of the shelf. They do not make it to the top however, as Bain sends arrows into several of them, while you drop rocks near at hand on the others. The wailing of the falling orcs cools the battle-lust of the mob below, and the drums are silent for a time.

"They will not come up this way again," says Bain "but they will use another tunnel or stair if there is one. We should act well while we can." You look around you, now that you have a moment to do so, and see that the bridge you stand next to leads off into a cave beyond. But it is what lies on your side of the chasm which is most interesting and more than a little surprising. "Look, Bain! It is what we have been seeking this whole time, and now it has come to us most unexpectedly." ***Move on to B1 (The Great Hall).***

354 **Time: 0**

The orc seems to be listening and looking down the passage away from you. He is short for an orc, not more than four and a half feet tall, but seems nearly as wide. His long, thick arms swing from massive shoulders, and almost touch the floor. He holds a curved sword, but you cannot see his face. There is some sort of emblem on the front of his leather armour, but the light is not bright enough for you to make out the details.

- *If you wait and observe the orc,* ***turn to 132.***
- *If you attack the orc,* ***turn to 207.***

355 **Time: 10** **Exp Pt: 2**

After minutes of searching, you locate a trap mechanism but are not certain as to how it works. Under Bain's watchful eye, you try to disarm it. Soon, the sound of sliding metal can be heard; you believe that the disarming has been successful. ***Pick a number*** *and add your Trickery bonus:*

- *If 2-6,* ***turn to 119.***
- *If 7-12,* ***turn to 183.***

356 **Time: 0**

Having been properly rebuked, you follow the dwarf until the ceiling begins to rise once more. Once you can both walk without bending over, you move ahead, patting Bain on the shoulder to reaffirm your camaraderie. "I am sorry," you offer.

"So am I," says Bain. "Our enemies are the orcs and my uncle's cousins, not each other. Let us keep that in mind." ***Turn to 352.***

3

357 **Time: 0**

Your leap was not long enough! With great effort you just manage to cling to the rock floor at the edge of the pit. It is impossible to dig your fingers into the stone surface. Your fingertips are torn as you try to find something to grasp. "Bain!" you call out, "Help me!" The dwarf did not fall into the pit and must not be far away. ***Pick a number*** *and add your General bonus:*

- *If 2-5,* ***turn to 366.***
- *If 6-12,* ***turn to 280.***

358 **Time: 0**

"The amulet! Let us see these foul creatures!"

As Bain draws forth the enchanted crystal, a grim sight is revealed in the pale light. You have been surrounded by black orcs who are now raising their weapons to attack. There is much hooting and howling and gnashing of broken teeth as the orcs advance. Bain cries out: "Put your back to mine and defend yourself!" ***Turn to 257.***

359 **Time: 5**

You are approaching an entrance which leads out onto a narrow ledge overlooking a vast rift which cuts through the mountain. ***Pick a number*** *and add your Intelligence Stat bonus:*

- *If 2-7,* ***turn to 360.***
- *If 8-12,* ***turn to 365.***

360 **Time: 0**

"Bain," you ask of your companion, "are there many such rifts in Moria, and are they bridged?"

"Rifts? Yes, there are many. And Durin's folk could not turn all of them into grand chambers, for some were unsuited and the rest were just far too large. As for bridges, I suppose we will discover any to be found."

The two of you walk out onto the ledge and stand in silence for a moment. The gulf before you is wide, and deep beyond reckoning. Great pinnacles of rock hang out of the vast distance above, or are thrust up from the depths below. The ledge you stand upon was obviously hewn out of the side of the sheer cliff which forms the wall of this side; it is a narrow way, and will not accommodate you shoulder-to-shoulder. There is a fluttering away above, but it is brief and soon out of mind. ***Pick a number*** *and add your Perception bonus:*

- *If 2-10,* ***turn to 336.***
- *If 11-12,* ***turn to 268.***

361 **Time: 10**

You move back into the shadows; the orc appears to be just a befuddled dark shape. After a few trying minutes, the goblin resumes alternately sharpening his knife and peering down the stairway. There is a noise behind you. As you press against the wall, you hear the unmistakable sound of orc-feet against the stone floor. More orcs!

9

Although the goblin in front of you must also hear the approaching footfalls, he seems to pay no attention to them. After a moment Bain touches your arm, and you see another dark figure approaching from behind. The creature is dressed like the other, also bearing a sword. He does not see you in the deep shadow of your hiding place and walks past. The two orcs grunt something unintelligible to each other, then the first leaves. Yet again, the two of you are missed.

Time passes; you cannot afford to wait any longer. Motioning for Bain to stay where he is, you prepare to attack. ***Turn to 207.***

362 **Time: N/A**

Nearing the end of your quest, you pause to count the hours and minutes to see if you and Bain will reach Bror's camp in time. *Total the Time elapsed since you first left the camp by the Celebrant River.*

- *If the Time elapsed brings you to Day 13 or earlier,* ***turn to 364.***
- *If the Time elapsed brings you to Day 14,* ***turn to 374.***
- *If the Time elapsed brings you to Day 15,* ***turn to 284.***
- *If the Time elapsed brings you to Day 16 or later,* ***turn to 161.***

363 **Time: 0**

You hear a rustling noise from somewhere above you. It seems to get louder and sounds, like the rubbing together of rough fabrics. "Perhaps it would be best to leave this place," cautions Bain.

- *If you leave the cave and continue up the main corridor you were traveling,* ***turn to 122.***
- *If you continue to explore the cavern,* ***turn to 127.***

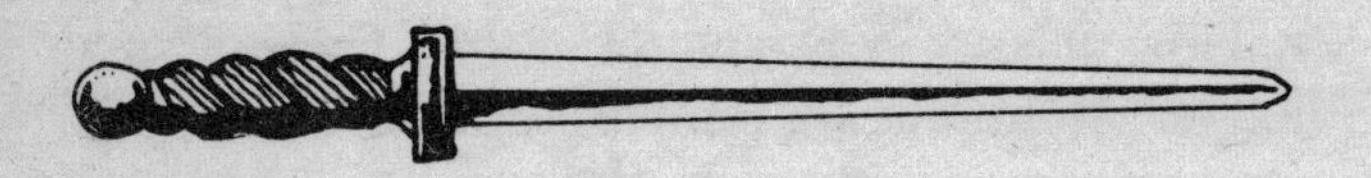

364 **Time: N/A**

Anxiously awaiting you and Bain near the trading site are Bror, son of Bram, and a fellow named Beren Longwood, a wealthy merchant and dealer.

Bror embraces Bain and asks you for the Will. When you produce it, the dwarf quickly inspects it, and to your surprise, breaks into a gay laughter. "This is it!" he cries. "I am forever at your service, friend. You have done very well indeed."

"Thank you," you say well pleased, for you know that dwarves rarely give their thanks and service.

With Bain beside him, Bror returns to the camp, gathers his followers, and confronts his greedy cousins. For a moment, you expect violence, but the just nature of Bror's claim — reinforced by the presence of the Will itself — prevails, and the usurpers back down.

7

Dressed elegantly in a long cloak and broad hat, Longwood greats you next. He proudly relates that he has dealt capably with the elves of Lórien on Bror's behalf and asks about booty you may have brought back from Moria. "I want everything you have, my friend," he says, his bright eyes aglitter, "if the price is... reasonable."

You laugh and ask for wine. After hours of haggling, threats and laughter, you agree upon the following prices for the listed items:

Map of the Endless Stair — 15 Silver coins
Doll — 2 Silver coins
Violet Powder — 4 Silver coins
Ring from The Forge — 10 Silver coins
Chain Armour from The Forge — 138 Gold coins
Bridge Plans — 9 Silver coins
Blue Diamond — 60 Gold coins
Brown Nut — 3 Silver coins

After filling your purse, you pause to eat supper and rest just beyond the camp-fire of the dwarves. Casually, Beren Longwood mentions another bold adventure on the horizon. Is there room in the party for another rogue you wonder, draining your cup. Only the next adventure will tell! **The End.**

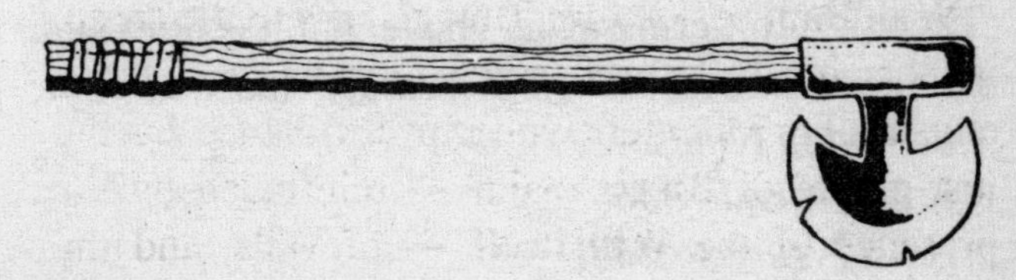

"Bain," you ask of your companion, "are there many such rifts in Moria, and are they bridged?"

"Rifts? Yes, there are many. And Durin's folk could not turn all of them into grand chambers, for some were unsuited and the rest were just far too large. As for bridges, I suppose we will discover any to be found."

You are about to walk out onto the ledge when you have a thought and turn to the dwarf. "Put your amulet aside for a few moments, Bain. We may not have our best view of the rift, but any cave-creatures will not have their best view of us. And I suspect that some will be about."

"Let me go ahead then, for my eyes are better suited to this work." The dwarf tucks the crystal under his tunic then feels his way along the tunnel out onto the ledge. You follow silently.

The gulf before you is wide, and deep beyond reckoning. Great pinnacles of rock hang out of the vast distance above or are thrust up from the depths below. The ledge you stand upon was obviously hewn out of the side of the sheer cliff which forms the wall of this side; it is a narrow way and will not accommodate you and Bain shoulder-to-shoulder. There is a fluttering away above, but it is brief and soon out of mind. ***Pick a number*** *and add your Perception bonus:*

- *If 2-7,* ***turn to 336.***
- *If 8-12,* ***turn to 268.***

366 **Time: N/A**

Deep within Moria, you fall endlessly to your death. Sadly, your quest is over. **The End.**

367 **Time: 10**

You move under the portcullis urging your companion to follow. Somewhat surprised that the gate stays wedged firmly in place, you hurry down the corridor. Occasional light-stones show the way. You step gingerly, trying to stir up as dust little as possible.

A short time later you discover that the tunnel runs up to a door. The door is of fine, smooth wood, but it no longer fits precisely into its warped frame.

- *If you enter through the door,* ***turn to 212.***
- *If you go back to the last junction,* ***turn to 120.***

368 **Time: 5** **Exp Pt: 55**

With one last mighty stroke, you smite the spider's wicked head, cleaving it in two.

"You have killed it!" declares Bain, though that is obvious as the dim light in its eyes is finally gone.

"We will not tarry here," you say. "This is a fell place. I fear the pit and what may lie underneath. Which way shall we go?"

The dwarf is still for a moment, then says, "There is a faint breeze coming from that direction." Bain waves his arm off to the left.

"Then we go that way." You both pass out of the spider's lair and begin to ascend a steeply sloping tunnel. ***Turn to 101.***

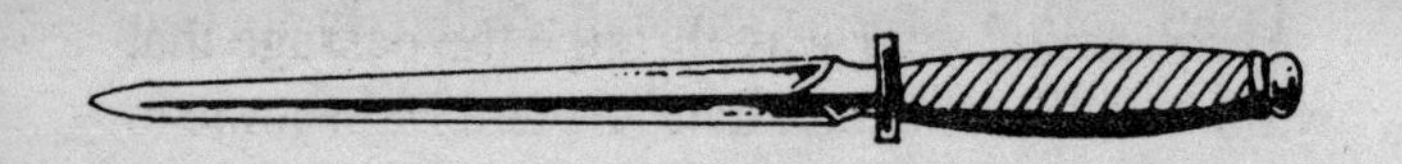

369 **Time: 5**

"Bain!" you cry to your companion. "Bain! This way!" You leap over your fallen foe with Bain not far behind, and more trolls right behind him! Blindly running down one passage, then another, you feel yourself becoming more and more disoriented.

"To the right!" calls Bain. Trusting his eyes, you turn and come out onto a ledge overlooking a wide grotto. The dwarf, bleeding and nearly out of breath, comes up a moment later. "We must find a tunnel too small for them to pursue."

"Let us hope we can find..." You are stopped by Bain who pushes you forward; the trolls are coming up from behind, beating the stone walls with their fists.

You begin to move along the ledge when Bain's crystal reveals yet another monstrous troll, this one a short distance off at the bottom of the cavern. As you watch in horror, it lifts a great rock hammer from its side and with raging bellow, hurls the missile at you. ***Pick a number*** *and subtract your DB:*

- *If 2-5,* ***turn to 206.***
- *If 6-12,* ***turn to 105.***

370 **Time: 10**

After forcing your way through the passage that was delved past the boulder, you and Bain come to a bridge over an aqueduct. The bridge is made of the finest marble and has no railing. Looking down at the underground watercourse, you note that the current appears to be quite swift. Bending low, you and the dwarf check the bridge for any traps that may be found. ***Pick a number*** *and add your Trickery bonus:*

- *If 2-5,* ***turn to 142.***
- *If 6-12,* ***turn to 147.***

371 **Time: 5**

Soon you come to a dark, hollow crack which opens into the face of rock on your left. Your pursuers, if indeed that is what they are, can not be seen behind since you have come around a great curving bend in the path.

- *If you enter into the crack off of the ledge,* ***turn to 107.***
- *If you pass by the crack and continue along the ledge,* ***turn to 322.***

372 **Time: N/A**

The swarming, vicious bats cause you to lose your footing and fall. They tear at you with their sharp claws while Bain, too, is overcome. You are defenseless and defeated! This quest has come to a sad conclusion. **The End.**

373 **Time: 5** **Exp Pt: 15**

The case opens. You reach in for the mithril coat, which feels smooth and cold against your hands as you pull it from its resting place. The armour is wonderfully made, though it is much too small for you. It must have been made for a young dwarf-prince. You notice that it is not completely finished: one arm is ragged and not as long as the other by a finger's length. *If you keep the Chain-mail, enter it on your Character Record.* ***Move on*** *to any "A" Location.*

374 **Time: N/A**

"May good fortune smile upon us!" you say to Bain. ***Pick a number:***

- *If 2-3,* ***turn to 319.***
- *If 4-12,* ***turn to 364.***

375 **Time: 10**

This shadowy passageway displays many different kinds of stonework, but those of the axe head and diamond designs are prevalent. Soon you arrive at a splitting of the corridor. ***Turn to 150.***

376 **Time: 0**

You rise to the top of this flight of stairs, but a grim sight meets you there. Another large band of goblins charge along the ledge from in front of you now, as well as behind. You are surrounded!

- *If you surrender,* ***turn to 115.***
- *If you fight those orcs that block your path ahead,* ***turn to 157.***

377 **Time: 40**

"Never mind," you say with little confidence. "We have come this far — we may just as well continue." The dwarf has little enthusiasm for this course of action but follows your lead in any event.

Onward you go, treading ever lower and deeper where the air is hotter and more stifling. The passage, if anything, becomes more complex in its twistings and switch-backs, though it descends steadily.

"We are lost, and that is Durin's truth," says the dwarf. "I have completely lost my bearings. I cannot tell how many levels we have descended, though I would say three or more at a guess."

"I am sorry now that we have come this way; it may be our undoing, but all we can do is continue."

Pick a number:

- *If 2-9,* ***turn to 290.***
- *If 10-12,* ***turn to 303.***

378 **Time: 0**

At this junction, two other archways serve to lead into two corridors. The first and largest arch is decorated with a vein of golden ore. The other displays a small rune composed of green crystal shards which have been imbedded into the stone.

- *If you go through the golden ore arch,* ***turn to 240.***
- *If you go through the green rune arch,* ***turn to 283.***

379 **Time: 5**

Manipulating the sides of the cube, shifting one then another, you manage to open it. Within, nestled in fleece is a small brown nut. Bain scratches his beard. "Curious," he says. ***Pick a number*** *and add your Perception bonus:*

- *If 2-5,* ***turn to 201.***
- *If 6-12,* ***turn to 229.***

380 **Time: 0**

A shaft leaps out of the heavy darkness, smiting you. ***Pick a number twice,*** *add the results together, and then increase your Damage Taken by that amount.*

- *If your Damage Taken now exceeds your Endurance value,* ***turn to 387.***
- *Otherwise,* ***turn to 395.***

381 **Time: 0**

You turn to make your way back down, but in your haste you fail to make sure of your footing. Your ankle twists painfully. As you collapse to one knee, you tumble forward and knock your head against a hard outcropping. Stumbling, you come back out into the cave. *Reduce your Running, Perception and OB bonuses by 1 each for the remainder of this adventure.* ***Turn to 220.***

382 **Time: N/A**

With confidence, you make to open the chest. But what a terrible mistake! You draw back your hand and inspect the trickle of blood running down your finger. A poisoned needle trap! You turn, ever slower, to your companion, Bain. His face swims in front of yours, and he speaks, but you cannot hear him. There is a dull crash against the back of your head; your view of the room's ceiling is your last. **The End.**

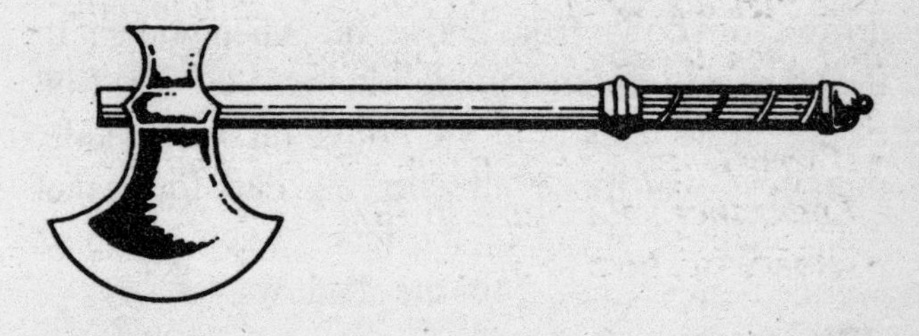

383 **Time: 10**

The two of run from the top of the stair along the ledge and into the waiting darkness. Unfortunately, you are still exposed to orcish archers on the other side of the rift, who continue to rain arrows down upon you. Seeking the safety of cover, you duck into a tunnel which has been delved from the pathway. It is dark and close, but with the dwarf close behind, you make your way along it. You soon discover that it curves around and down to the left, but the orc-cries coming down from the rear urge you on.

The tunnel ends perhaps fifty feet below where it started and it has come out to a bridge which spans the rift in two sections; the first leading out to a rocky column rising out of the Deep while the second extends the path over to the other side of the chasm. You hear orcs coming down the tunnel, and the ever-steady 'thrum, thrum!' of their drums continues to echo up and down the gulf. "The bridge, let us go!" gasps the dwarf who is nearly out of breath.

You run along the thin stone pathway as more arrows rain down from above, but when you get to the other side, another tunnel shelters you. The first of the orc-torches light the bridge on the far side, though you can make out scurrying, dark forms that have chanced ahead of the rest. "Keep going..." comes Bain's voice from the shadows.

"Are you sorely hurt?"

The dwarf steps forward into the light of the crystal and although he is bleeding from many wounds, he says, "I can follow."

You begin to run again, but when this tunnel comes to its end, you fear you have too. The orc-passage opens out onto the rift again, but the bridge that was once here has long since fallen into the gorge. A sheer precipice drops away at your feet. "No!" you wail.

From beside you, Bain looks up and through the void sees a bridge and landing no more than a hundred feet above you. "We must go that way," he says.

6

"Are you mad? We cannot fly but perhaps you have sprouted wings since last I saw you in daylight."

"There is no time for jest with the orcs so close behind. Look here," and the dwarf shows you the rift wall near the tunnel's mouth. "There are handholds here. Goblin-made, but useful. We must use them to climb up to the next level or the orcs will surely have their way with us here." You look up in despair but see that the climb could be made. The wall is not quite so sheer, and the hand-holds look sturdy enough. The bridge above certainly looks more inviting than the depths below.

"You first Bain. Here is the crystal." You give it back and say, "You must find the best way and let us hope the holds do not stop half-way up!"

Turn to 407.

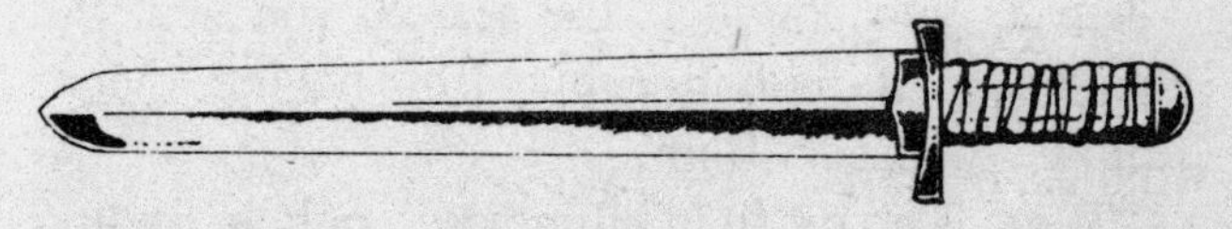

384 **Time: 0**

The desk has two drawers which do not appear to have locks. You may explore each of the following options only once.

- *If you further examine the top of desk,* ***turn to 168.***
- *If you open the first drawer,* ***turn to 394.***
- *If you open the second drawer,* ***turn to 219.***
- *Otherwise,* ***move on*** *to any "A" Location.*

385 **Time: 5**

The orc-arrows have all missed you, though they did come rather close to the mark! You have climbed beyond the range of their missiles, so lithe and strong goblin-warriors now begin to ascend after you. Fortunately, you arrive at the landing where Bain stands before they can close to within an arms reach, and for his part, the dwarf has already prepared his own bow. ***Turn to 353.***

386 **Time: 5** **Exp Pt: 10**

You have defeated the goblin! Despite the horrible odour, you decide to search the fallen orc. Bain keeps an eye out for other goblins while you go through the small pack at the creature's side. Therein, you find some dirty twine, a piece of dry bone, a knife, and a leather bag holding what must be orc-food; foul and disgusting.

Just as you complete the search, you hear the sound of footfalls approaching from behind. "More follow," whispers Bain.

"There is no profit in killing orcs, only in finding the Will," you say, hurrying down the steps with Bain close behind. *Add any items you wish to keep from the orc's equipment to your Character Record.* ***Turn to 330.***

387 **Time: N/A**

Struck down by a black orcish arrow, your quest comes to an end, for Bain cannot save you. **The End.**

388 **Time: 5** **Exp Pt: 30**

Sorely wounded, the giant spider retreats down one of its accursed tunnels with one eye blind and a severed claw left behind.

"That was handy work!" says the dwarf, "and it is a good time for us to leave this place! I have unwittingly been cast into the pit and I would not return there if given the choice."

"I am with you, but which way should we go? Let us choose before the wretched thing returns!"

The dwarf is still for a moment, then says, "There is a faint breeze coming from that direction." Bain waves his arm off to the left.

"Then we go that way." You both pass out of the spider's lair and begin to ascend a steeply sloping tunnel. ***Turn to 101.***

389 **Time: 5**

Bain holds out his amulet to reveal the room you stand in.

It is a small chamber littered with barrels, and through its centre is a fast-flowing flume of water. "This is one of Moria's emergency escape routes," informs Bain. "It is peculiar, I admit, but useful, as we shall see."

"I hope so," you offer. "It will not take long for those orcs to figure that we did not disappear into thin air. If we are not gone for good, they will have us." There is a pounding on the wall behind you.

Bain rushes over to one of the larger barrels with a metal top. "This should serve us well," he says. "Get in!"

"Into that barrel? Do you propose that we just ride out of Moria in a girding of wood through an underground stream?"

"I do," he retorts, "and if you will not come, I shall go alone." The drums roar outside and begin to echo through this chamber.

"Very well, as it appears I have no other choice."

"In that, you are correct," says the dwarf. "Now, let us get this barrel closer to the watercourse." You help Bain move the contraption over to the flume, then step into it. Fortunately there is enough room for both of you inside, because Bain enters before closing the top. With a rocking motion, he tips the barrel over into the rushing stream.

"This ride I will not soon forget," you say as the two of you turn over and over inside of the container, occasionally striking an outcropping of rock but always moving faster through the speeding waterway. ***Turn to 169.***

390 **Time: 5**

"I wish to have a closer look at it," you tell Bain.

"But why?" he asks. "I fear we tarry here too long."

"I thought that I had made it clear: I have the final say in all things while we carry out this special mission for your uncle," you assert. "Now come with me."

The two of you draw up to the old cart, which is girded in rusting iron. Looking inside, you find half of a load of dusty ore-veined rock. "It must have been abandoned when your folk left this part of Moria," you say to Bain, who looks about nervously.

"I have a bad feeling," he says. "This is a fell place. My council is that we leave, soon!"

"A moment," you reply. "We have yet to see if any other corridors lead from this one. What if one of them is the only way for us to find the main passage leading to the Great Hall? Listening to you, we would miss it and go back to Bror empty-handed, without the Will."

- *If you think Bain is a fool,* ***turn to 276.***
- *If you return to the last intersection on Bain's advice,* ***turn to 346.***

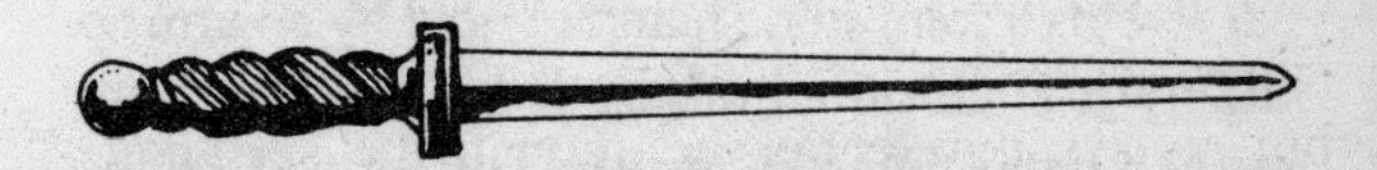

391 **Time: 15**

"The tunnel, Bain," you decide. "Who knows what could be lurking in the cave."

After the two of you proceed down the tunnel, Bain whispers so that you can barely hear him: "If lurking is to be done, cave or tunnel makes no difference..."

Once again the stone scraping sounds reach you, but this time it is closer. Bain quickens his pace. Being small and sure-footed, he gets uncomfortably ahead of you. "Bain!" you call out in as low a voice as you can muster. "Bain! Slow down. I can barely see you." The faint glimmer of light he carries disappears and reappears with the winding of the tunnel. Although you seem to be getting closer now, so do the sounds of grinding rock. Then there is a howl which freezes your blood to ice. Unearthly it is, and pained — it rolls down your corridor, causing Bain to stop and turn. There is fear in his eyes.

"What is it?" you ask as you finally come up to him.

The answer is unnecessary, for it stands only a short way down the tunnel in front of the dwarf. Dark and huge it is, with large pale black eyes and gaping maw. A cave-troll!

It wields a long stone hammer held by an arm so mighty it could mold the earth itself. It cries out again, but this time it is answered by several others. You are about to be surrounded! ***Pick a number:***

- *If 2,* ***turn to 312.***
- *If 3-6,* ***turn to 287.***
- *If 7-12,* ***turn to 106.***

392 **Time: 20**

You travel for some time, but the corridor still stretches before you into the gloom.

"This is a good place to stop for a few moments and rest," you say, loosening your knapsack.

The dwarf responds. "A good place this is not! Make no sudden movement. Do you see this stonework here, and the chisel lines in the wall behind you?"

Once pointed out, you quickly affirm Bain's observations. "What of them?" you ask.

"Clever dwarf-work. This corridor has been trapped by my ancestors, and though normally inactive, I can tell that it has been reset recently. No orc would know the secret of it. Carefully now, follow me, and I may see us both through." ***Pick a number** and add your Trickery bonus:*

- *If 2-6, **turn to 253.***
- *If 7-12, **turn to 349.***

393 **Time: 0**

As you pick up the delicate band it breaks in two, for the years have weakened it with corrosion. You regretfully examine the useless pieces and drop them to the floor.

"Shoddy workmanship," says Bain. "There is nothing for it." ***Move on** to any "A" Location.*

394 **Time: 5**

You open the drawer and discover a large cube of wood. The block appears solid, but when you move it, something rattles inside. Taking the cube, Bain turns it over and over looking for a way to open it. ***Pick a number** and add your Perception bonus:*

- *If 2-7, **turn to 397.***
- *If 8-12, **turn to 379.***

395 **Time: 0**

You have been struck by a black orcish arrow, but are still alive. Bain's armour turns the one which has been lofted at him, but he has no interest in having his chain shirt tested again. "Quickly, away from here!" he cries.

- *If you follow Bain's advice and run,* ***turn to 296.***
- *If you wish for you and Bain to stay and fight these orcs,* ***turn to 234.***

396 **Time: 30**

Awakening to the dim light of the Forge chamber, your head is throbbing, your stomach churning. "I must admit that I am glad to see you recover," says Bain, though his voice sounds somewhat distant.

"I feel... fine." You try to sound convincing, but Bain is not easily fooled, though he helps you get to your feet without further comment. ***Turn to 195.***

397 **Time: 10**

After examining the cube for some time, you both admit that it is impossible to open.

"Confound it!" you exclaim. "There is no good in it." Leaving the wooden block where you found it, you continue with the search. ***Turn to 384.***

398 **Time: 5**

You walk through the entrance and stare in awe at the huge cavern. Colourful fluted columns striking up from the floor and glistening pendants hanging from the roof overhead construct a wild landscape of towering shapes.

6

"Beware," you warn, "our enemies could be nearby. With all of this rock strewn about, they could easily be waiting in ambush." Both you and Bain take pains to ensure that no one is waiting here for you. Once you have finished, a bridge crossing another dark chasm appears ahead.

"If they are not here, I would guess they wait to welcome us on the far side of that pit," says Bain in a dire voice. ***Turn to 344.***

399 **Time: 0**

Ablack dart passes you to one side, barely missing. "We have awoken orcs here!" cries Bain. "Quickly, we should run while we still can!" He grabs at your arm to bring you back out onto the ledge.

- *If you follow Bain's advice and run,* ***turn to 296.***
- *If you wish for you and Bain to stay and fight these orcs,* ***turn to 234.***

400 **Time: 5**

You carefully pull the ring out from under the pallet. It is beautifully worked, having the look of silver but without tarnish, despite the fact that it must have been here for some time. Without a second thought, and before Bain can warn you to the contrary, you slide the band onto your finger. ***Pick a number*** *and add your Magical bonus:*

- *If 2-6,* ***turn to 310.***
- *If 7-12,* ***turn to 277.***

8

401 **Time: 10**

This corridor takes you to a dimly lit grotto. From within, you feel a cool dampness and hear a distant, slow dripping which echoes from what you would guess to be a still pool in the distance.

- *If you enter the cave, **turn to 110.***
- *If you go back to the last intersection and continue down the main passage into the water, **turn to 175.***

402 **Time: 0**

Some hideous and shadowy form quickly comes up behind the two of you in absolute, deadly silence. *In the following combat, you are Surprised.* ***Turn to 189.***

403 **Time: 0**

There are too many of the black orcs to overcome. You call for Bain to leave the cave with you, and soon you both are running along the ledge which skirts the bottomless chasm; many more goblins chase at your heals. ***Turn to 197.***

404 **Time: 0**

"Perhaps it is not trapped at all," you say. "I can find no sign of one."

"Nor can I," confirms Bain. "The Great Hall lies beyond. I am going."

You follow Bain across the bridge. ***Turn to 238.***

405 **Time: N/A**

With a sweeping blow, you are knocked from the ledge and fall over the precipice into the Deeps of Moria. Your quest ends in a cruel and unfortunate death. **The End.**

406 **Time: 0** **Exp Pt: 75**

Two orcs lie dead at your feet while another pair have been cast over the precipice, thanks to the powerful strokes of your weapon. The other goblins ahead judge you a foe too powerful for their meagre skills and run off.

Calling back to Bain that the way is now clear, he casts aside his foe and runs up behind you despite the many who remain to give chase. ***Turn to 383.***

407 **Time: 5**

Bain begins his climb while you look back down the tunnel for approaching torches. "Follow me now," calls down Bain, who has already managed to get up a fair distance. You set your foot into the first hollow prepared by the orcs just for such travel and grab another with your hand above. The climb is easier than you had expected though that is of little comfort: orcs have come out onto the landing below you. Despite the first of them tumbling into the gorge with the weight of the others behind, they call back into their ranks while the drums continue their 'thrum, thrum!'. They have brought forward their archers, and you are an easy target! Three of them lift their bows and draw the strings taught.

"Bain, they are shooting!" ***Pick a number*** *and subtract your DB:*

- *If 2-7,* ***turn to 385.***
- *If 8-12,* ***turn to 208.***

408 **Time: 0** **Exp Pt: 5**

You open the lock silently, then release Bain's with a 'click'. The orc-commander seems to have noticed your activity but the two arguing goblins are so intent that they accidentally block the larger orc as he tries to grab Bain: now is your chance to escape! You stand and run for the top of the stairs, the closest escape route. ***Turn to 256.***

409 **Time: 5**

You hear a sharp, sudden noise; the dwarf did not make it. Stopping still as stone, you listen, but no other sound follows.

Bain begins to edge towards the dark crack ahead, and you too move to gain the wall. You and the dwarf stand motionless against the side of the cave, feeling the dampness of the stone and peering into the blackness. A darker shape moves slightly, and you realize that an orc is standing in the passageway. He moves to the side, and you can see him more clearly. ***Pick a number*** *and add your Trickery bonus:*

- *If 2-6,* ***turn to 207.***
- *If 7-12,* ***turn to 354.***

410 **Time: 0**

The papers are carefully rendered jewelry designs which Bain clearly desires. "They are of no interest to me," you say, passing the sheets to the dwarf. ***Turn to 307.***

411 **Time: 10**

Just before you start moving along your ledge, you see torches spring to life on the other side of the gulf. Dark forms hold them aloft, and many of them are bobbing in the distance now like a procession of malevolent fireflies. They enter a deep shadow just within view far to the right, then turn. There is a bridge, and they are crossing it!

"If they come this way, we are doomed no matter who, or what they are," you say. "It seems there is no comfort for us in Moria."

"True enough," replies the dwarf. "We should follow this path." He gestures to the left.

"I agree, but give me your crystal first, for I will lead; in the dark I would surely miss a crack or slide. That would send me deep into a place I would rather not go!"

Bain gives you the amulet on its heavy chain, and turning, you hurry off along the pathway; a steep wall rising to your left, and a sheer cliff dropping away to the right. ***Turn to 371.***

412 **Time: 5**

Bain is about to push the portal open when you hear heavy footsteps from behind. You both turn to see two heavily armoured dwarves with sharp, steel axes cross the Hall. Bain removes the rune-key and stuffs it into his tunic.

"Do not hide the key," says one of the approaching dwarves. "We know the secret and can find the Will of Old Bror for ourselves. Give it to us!"

11

Then to the first dwarf, you raise your voice and challenge him: "Who comes upon us so — at unawares and with weapons bared? Speak!"

"Do not play the fool," he growls from under a reddish beard. "You are here for the Will, and so are we, but it is we who shall have it. Now give us the key!"

Bain pulls the axe from his belt and steps forward. "You must kill me first, and even then I would curse you, for the Will is well hidden within the vault beyond. You cannot find the Will. Only I know were it is, and I will not say!"

Then the first dwarf takes another step ahead and approaches Bain. He begins to speak in the secret tongue of the dwarves, Khuzdul, at first quietly, then ending with an overwhelming shout. Bain responds in kind, and it sounds as if the two are trading uncouth insults. The first dwarf shifts the axe in his hands just before Bain takes a mighty swing with his! Battle is joined; there is no stopping them. The second dwarf raises his weapon and charges you with a yell.

You must fight this dwarf and may not Run Away.

(**DWARF** OB:4 DB:3 EP:30)

- *If you defeat the dwarf,* ***turn to 232.***
- *If the dwarf knocks you unconscious,* ***turn to 273.***
- *If the dwarf kills you,* ***turn to 148.***

With a gentle push, Bain opens the concealed portal and a dark corridor, low and narrow, is revealed beyond.

You pass down its short length and come into a small chamber. The Vault of Bram! Before you rest a wooden chest, an iron-bound trunk, a metal coffer and a tall urn, painted and fired. Three short pillars support the roof and Bain makes for these. You are free to examine the containers; a rare joy that is!

Before you reach the first one though, a distant 'Thrum, thrum!' can be heard. "Hurry," you say to Bain. "Orcs have found their way to this Great Hall. Those are the drums of doom!"

You have just enough time to search only one of the containers.

- *If you go to the chest,* ***turn to 298.***
- *If you go to the trunk,* ***turn to 156.***
- *If you go to the coffer,* ***turn to 338.***
- *If you go to the urn,* ***turn to 163.***

CREATING A CHARACTER

If you do not want to create your own character, use the pre-created character found just before the prologue.

If you decide to create your own character, you must follow the directions given in this section. Keep track of your character on the *Character Record* found following this section. It is advisable to enter information in pencil so that it can be erased and updated. If necessary, you may copy or photocopy this Character Record for your own use.

As you go through this character creation process, refer to the pre-created character found just before the prologue.

STATS

Your character starts with certain mental and physical attributes called "stats" (short for statistics): Strength (St), Agility (Ag), and Intelligence (In). Before beginning this adventure, determine the values of these stats. ***Pick a number*** 3 times, assign one to each of the three stats, and record them in the *Stat Value* column on your Character Record.

Stat Bonuses

Each stat (St, Ag, In) may give a "bonus" when performing certain activities; keep in mind that these "bonuses" can be negative (or zero) as well as positive.

Each stat of **2-4** gives a bonus of **-1**
Each stat of **5-8** gives a bonus of **+0** (i.e., no bonus)
Each stat of **9-10** gives a bonus of **+1**
Each stat of **11-12** gives a bonus of **+2**

Record these bonuses in the *Stat Bonus* column next to the *Stat Values* on your Character Record.

Applying Stat Bonuses to Skills

In the *Skill* section on your character record there is also a *Stat Bonus* column. Each space has a stat abbreviation next to it; in each space record the stat bonus corresponding to the abbreviation. (Refer to the pre-created character if you need help in following these instructions.)

ENDURANCE

Your Strength stat determines the *Endurance* of your character. During combat you will take damage due to shock, pain, bleeding, etc. If this "Damage Taken" exceeds your *Endurance* you will fall unconscious (pass out). Your *Endurance* is equal to:

20 plus twice your Strength stat.

Record this on your Character Record.

SKILLS

The following 8 "skills" affect your chances of accomplishing certain actions during your adventures.

1) *Melee OB Skill:* This skill reflects your ability to attack in melee (hand-to-hand) combat. OB stands for "Offensive Bonus".
2) *Missile OB Skill:* This skill reflects your ability to attack using a missile such as a thrown spear or a bow. OB stands for "Offensive Bonus" (not used in the Basic System).
3) *General Skill:* Use this skill when directed to perform general activities by the text, including: Climb, Track, Hunt, Ride, and Swim actions.
4) *Trickery Skill:* Use this skill when trying to move without being seen or heard (i.e., sneaking), trying to steal or take something held or protected by an opponent, picking a lock, escaping from bonds, and other similar activities.
5) *Perception Skill:* This skill reflects how much information you gather through observation and exploration. It also reflects your ability to talk and negotiate with beings that you meet during your adventures.
6) *Magical Skill:* This skill reflects your affinity with magic and spells. You use this skill when you try to cast a spell and when indicated by the text.
7) *Running Skill:* This skill reflects your chances of running away from danger.
8) *DB Skill:* This skill reflects your ability to avoid attacks. DB stands for "Defensive Bonus".

Skill Bonuses

For each of these skills, you will have a *Skill Bonus* used when you attempt certain actions. Keep in mind that these "bonuses" can be negative as well as positive.

- When you start your character, you have 6 "+1 bonuses" to assign to your skills; the choice is yours (see below). These bonuses may **not** be assigned to your "DB" skill or your "Running" skill.
- You may assign more than one "+1 bonuses" to a given skill, but no more than three to any one skill. Thus, two "+1 bonuses" assigned to a skill will be a "+2 bonus," and three "+1 bonuses" will be a "+3 bonus". These bonuses should be recorded in the appropriate spaces in the Skill Bonus column on your Character Record.
- If you do not assign any "+1 bonuses" to a skill, record a "-2 bonus" in the appropriate space. The "DB" and "Running" skills do **not** receive this "-2 bonus".

TOTAL BONUSES

At this point, you should have a bonus recorded in each *Stat Bonus* space and each *Skill Bonus* space; keep in mind that these "bonuses" can be negative as well as positive. For each skill, add the two bonuses and record the total in the appropriate **TOTAL BONUS** space.

When the text instructs you to "add your bonus," it is referring to these *Total Bonuses*.

During play, you may acquire equipment or abilities that may affect your bonuses. The *Special Bonus* space may be used to record these bonuses; of course, some of the *Total Bonuses* will have to be recalculated when this occurs.

SPELLS

You may decide to use the *Optional Spell Rules*. If so, for every "+1 bonus" that you do not assign to a skill, you may "learn" two spells that you may cast during play (see *Optional Rules* at the end of this gamebook).

THE ADVANCED *QUESTGAME*™ SYSTEM

If you are going to use the Basic System do not read any further.

The Advanced System is similar to the Basic System in many respects, but it allows for more variety and action options.

TIME

Keeping track of time adds a great deal of flavour and excitement to the use of this *Gamebook*, but it does require that you keep a running total of the amount of time that passes. If you desire an easier adventure, just use the gamebook as directed and ignore the text passages and rules referring to time (see the Basic System).

Passage of time will be abbreviated at the beginning of each text section as: *Time:* #, where # is the number of minutes. As you read each text section, add this amount to your time total.

TAKING AN ACTION

When the text directs you to ***take an action***, refer to the *Action Table* at the end of this gamebook. Choose one of the actions listed and follow the directions given.

EQUIPMENT

You may only wear: 1 suit of armour, 1 dagger (on belt), 1 cloak, 1 backpack, and 1 belt and pouch.

In addition, you may **carry** a number of pieces of equipment equal to your *Strength* stat; this total may include a maximum of 3 weapons. If you lose your backpack, this number is reduced by half (round down), and you lose any excess equipment along with the backpack.

Certain special items indicated by the text may be obtained that do not follow these restrictions.

- **Weapons:** If you damage an opponent, your weapon can provide **additional damage** (this additional damage applies to each attack only when a damage result of 1 or more is obtained):

Weapon	Damage	Note
Sword	+1	
Mace	+2	(only if opponent is wearing chain or plate armour)
Spear	+0	
Dagger	-1	
Warhammer	+2	(but -1 to melee OB)
Battle-axe	+2	
Quarterstaff	+1	
Two-hand Sword	+3	(but -1 to melee OB)
Bare-handed	-3	(and -2 to melee OB)

EXAMPLE: *Using the Combat Table, you inflict "8" damage on your opponent. If you are using a sword (+1 to damage), your opponent actually takes 9 damage points ("8" +1). If you are using a Dagger (-1 to damage), he would take 7 damage points ("8" -1).*

- **Thrown Weapons:** The following weapons may be used once in a given combat as a missile attack (missile OB modifications are given in parentheses: spear(-1), dagger(-1), warhammer(-2), sword(-3), mace(-3), battle-axe(-4). In such a case, the weapon may not be used in melee and may only be recovered if you defeat your opponent.
- A **bow** may only be used in missile combat (see step 1 under **Fighting**), not in melee combat.
- A **shield** may **not** be used in combination with the following weapons: bow, battle-axe, quarterstaff, or two-hand sword.
- **Armour** has the following effects on your skill bonuses:

Plate Armour: +3 to DB; -3 to Trickery, Running, and Magical bonuses

Chain Armour: +2 to DB; -2 to Trickery, Running, and Magical bonuses

Leather Armour: +1 to DB; -1 to Trickery and Running bonuses

 Shield: +1 to DB; -1 to Magical bonus

FIGHTING

Fighting consists of a series of "rounds." During each "round," you attack your opponent *or* you attempt to flee **and** your opponent attacks you.

If you choose to fight an opponent **or** the text indicates that you "must fight," the combat is resolved in the following fashion:

1) If you are surprised, proceed directly to step 4; otherwise, proceed to step 2.
2) You **may** make a missile attack if able (see the attack resolution explanation). If your opponent is not surprised (i.e., he is aware of you), he will then make a missile attack against you if able (the text will specify if your opponent can make a missile attack).

   This completes one **round** *of the fight.*
3) No one is surprised for the remainder of the combat. Your opponent will attempt to force melee (hand-to-hand combat). If you wish to continue making missile attacks, ***pick a number*** *and add your Running bonus*. If the result is 10 or greater, proceed to step 2; otherwise, proceed to step 4.
4) You are engaged in melee. You make a melee attack against your opponent, and he makes a melee attack against you. If you are surprised, the order of the attacks is reversed.

   This completes one **round** *of the fight.*

5) Repeat rounds of the fight until one of the following conditions occur:

   a) One of you is **killed** (a "K" result on the Combat Table); or

   b) One of you has more *Damage Taken* than *Endurance*. That combatant is **unconscious** and is defeated. (This can also occur due to a "U" result on the Combat Table.) or

   c) You successfully **disengage.** At the beginning of any round of combat, you may elect not to attack for that round. After your opponent makes his attack for that round, you may ***pick a number*** *and add your Running bonus*:

      - If the result is 9 or greater, you successfully *Run Away* (follow text instructions).
      - Otherwise, you are still engaged and must begin another round of the fight at step 4. (However, you may attempt to *disengage* again).

Resolve individual attacks as indicated in the Basic System: Using the Combat Table at the end of this gamebook, cross-index the difference in OB and DB with a number picked. Use your character's Missile OB for a missile attack and Melee OB for a melee attack.

DAMAGE AND HEALING

Keep track of *Damage Taken* as indicated in the Basic System. If your *Damage Taken* exceeds your *Endurance* (see your Character Record), you are unconscious. If this occurs during a fight, you are **defeated** and must proceed as the text indicates. If the text indicates that you "wake up," reduce your *Damage Taken* to equal your *Endurance*.

Do not use the Basic System rule for healing. Each time you read a section of text that does not require you to ***pick a number***, fight, or ***take an action***, you may reduce your *Damage Taken* by 1 for every 20 minutes you spend "resting".

OPTIONAL RULES

These rules are included to allow you to develop more complete Middle-earth characters and to add certain elements of realism to your *QuestGame*™ adventures.

CASTING SPELLS

For every "+1 bonus" that you do **not** assign to a skill during the character creation process, you may "learn" two of the spells described below. Once a spell is "learned," your character "knows" it and is able to cast it within the restrictions given below.

- If you want to cast a spell, ***pick a number*** *and add your Magical bonus*. If the result is 7 or greater, you successfully cast the spell. (Refer to the spell description for the effects.) Otherwise, the spell has no effect. You must "know" a spell in order to cast it.
- Each time you successfully cast a spell, your *Damage Taken* is increased by the number given in parentheses in the spell description. This reflects the strain of casting spells.
- If involved in a fight, you may only attempt to cast a spell when a missile would normally be fired; spells are impossible to cast when engaged in melee (exception: Speed).
- Unless stated otherwise, the effects of a spell last for one action, one activity, or one fight.

Spell Descriptions

1) **Item Analysis** (3): When told to by the text, you may cast this spell and "analyze" an item (follow the directions given in the text).
2) **Balance** (2): Increases your *General* bonus by +2 for one activity to be attempted at the current text location.
3) **Calm** (5): May only be cast against one animal or normal being (Man, Elf, Dwarf, Hobbit, Orc, Troll, etc.). ***Pick a number*** *and add your Magical bonus*. If the result is 8 or

more, the foe is "calmed," so you may automatically *Run Away*. Otherwise, the encounter proceeds normally. If an encounter does not provide a *Run Away* opportunity in the choice selection, the opponent may not be "calmed." This spell may not be cast if you are facing multiple foes.

4) **Camouflage** (3): For the purposes of **one** action, this spell increases your *Trickery* bonus by +2.

5) **Charm Animal** (6): You may cast this spell against any hostile normal "animal" (bear, wolf, snake, etc.). Proceed through the text as if you had defeated the animal. The animal will follow you (record its OB, DB, and *Endurance*) and will fight any foe you desire it to. After it has been involved in one fight for you, the animal will leave. You may only have one animal "charmed" at a time.

6) **Clairvoyance** (5): When given a **choice** of two or more text sections to read, you may read two of them and then proceed to the one you prefer.

7) **Fire Bolt** (6): This spell may be used during combat when you would normally make a missile attack. ***Pick a number*** *and add double your Magical bonus*; the result is the amount of *Damage Taken* by one opponent of your choice.

8) **Healing** (0): Reduces the amount of time required to heal 3 points of damage from 60 minutes to 20 minutes. Using this spell and resting for a "night" heals all damage.

9) **Luck** (5): When you cast this spell just after you have ***picked a number***, you may ignore the number picked and ***pick a number*** again. This spell may not cast more than once per text passage.

10) **Protection from Magic** (4): When the text indicates that an opponent is casting a spell, you may cast this spell. The number picked to resolve his spell will be decreased by your *Magical* bonus.

11) **Shield** (4): If cast at the beginning of a fight, this spell will increase your *DB* by +2. This spell may not be cast if you will be using a normal shield during the combat.

12) **Speed** (3): This spell may be cast whenever you attempt to **Run Away**, or **disengage from a fight**. Your *Running* bonus is increased by +2 for such attempts. This is the only spell that may be cast while engaged in melee.

13) **Strength** (6): When cast at the beginning of a fight, this spell doubles the damage you give with melee attacks for the remainder of the fight. "U" and "K" results are unaffected by a Strength spell.

14) **Sustain Self** (2): When cast, this spell has the same effect as eating a meal.

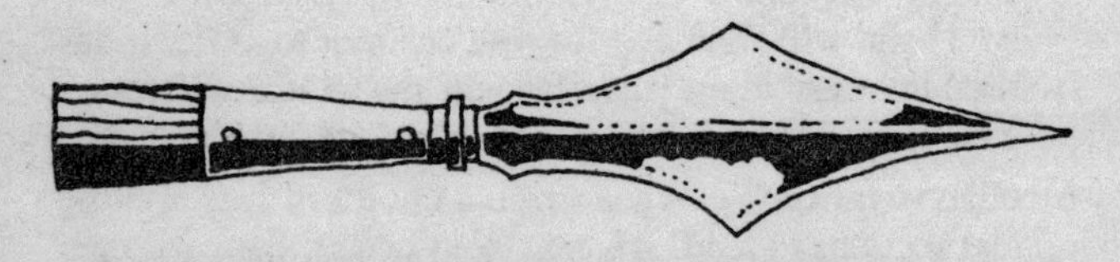

EXPERIENCE POINTS

After certain text passages, you will see *Exp Pt: #*. This is the number of "Experience Points" you receive. Keep a running total of points in the space provided on your Character Record. You may only receive experience points for a given text passage once.

These points have no affect on the abilities of your character until you have successfully completed this adventure and wish to start another ***MEQ Gamebook*** with the same character.

If you are using a ***MEQ Gamebook*** character, for every 150 experience points you may choose one of these options:

1) Assign an additional +1 bonus to any of the allowed skills (see "Creating Your Own Character") **or**
2) You may change any "-2" skill bonus to "+1" **or**
3) You may choose two more spells that you may cast **or**
4) You may pick a number and increase your *Endurance* by 2 plus that number.

If you are using ***MERP***, 150 experience points is equivalent to approximately 5000 ***MERP*** experience points.

RACE

You may choose one of the Middle-earth races for your character with the following results:

Man: Increase your *General* bonus by 1.

Elf: When underground, decrease your *Perception* by 1 and your *Magical* bonus by 1. When outdoors, increase your *Perception* by 1 and your *Magical* bonus by 1.

Dwarf: Decrease your Running bonus by 1. When underground, increase your *Perception* bonus by 1 and your *General* bonus by 1. Dwarves may not "learn" spells #7 and #11.

Hobbit: Increase your *Trickery* bonus by 2. Decrease your *Melee OB* by 2. Hobbits may not "learn" spells #3, #5, #7, and #11.

AN OPTIONAL COMBAT FORMULA

For people who prefer formulas to tables, the following formula approximates the Combat Table's results. Using the formula results in slightly more damage than using the table.

- If the number picked is "2", automatic no damage.
- If the number picked is "12", automatic "U" plus normal Damage Taken.
- Otherwise, the Damage Taken by defender = ***Number picked*** - 4 + attacker's OB - defender's DB **and**
  - If Damage Taken is 9 or more = "U"
  - If Damage Taken is 11 or more = "K"

UNMODIFIED *PICKED* NUMBERS

In many situations, you are instructed to: ***Pick a number and add your xxxx bonus***. If you have a very large (or very small) bonus, this can often result in automatic success (or failure) in certain activities. To avoid this, use the following rule: whenever you ***pick a number*** and it is a "2" or a "12", do not add any bonuses. That is, 2's and 12's are never modified: a 2 always gives a 2 result and a 12 always gives a 12 result.

USING *MERP* WITH THIS GAMEBOOK

Middle-earth Role Playing is ICE's fantasy role playing (FRP) system for J.R.R. Tolkien's Middle-earth. We do not have room is this gamebook to describe its contents. Instead we will give guide-lines in this section on how to use this gamebook with a ***MERP*** character.

Since ***MERP*** is a general FRP system, you will have to be very flexible when using it with these gamebook. Just use the mechanisms provided by M***ERP*** and some common sense, and most situations will be easily resolved. Below we provide guide-lines for the situations which arise most often in these gamebooks.

USING BONUSES

During play you are often instructed to: ***pick a number*** *and add your xxxx bonus*, where *xxxx* is Running, General, Trickery, Perception, or Magical. Then you are given two or more possible places to ***turn to*** based upon the result.

When using ***MERP***, use these corresponding ***MERP*** "Skill Bonuses" instead of the bonus indicated:

QuestGame™ **Bonus**	***MERP* Skill Bonus**
Running	Moving Manoeuvre based upon armour worn
General	Climb, Ride, Swim, or Track
Trickery	Ambush, Stalk/Hide, Pick Lock, or Disarm Trap
Perception	Perception, Leadership & Influence
Magical	Read Runes, Use Item, or Make a Resistance Roll

The circumstances of the text passage being read usually make the specific ***MERP*** bonus obvious (e.g., if the passage says you are attempting to "swim", you will use your ***MERP*** Swim Skill Bonus). If it is not obvious, use the skill that seems most appropriate.

When you use a ***MERP*** Skill Bonus divide by 10 (round down). For example, a ***MERP*** Swim Skill Bonus of 36 would be used in this gamebook as a +3 *General* bonus in appropriate situations.

Fighting

When the text indicates that you must fight, just use the normal ***MERP*** combat system, your character's ***MERP*** combat stats, and your opponents' ***MERP*** combat stats (as given in the ***MERP*** **Stats Table** found near the end of this book).

Like normal *QuestGame*™ fights, fights resolved using ***MERP*** normally end in one of 3 ways: you are defeated, your opponent is defeated, or you successfully *Run Away.*

Either you or your opponent is "defeated" when you are rendered unconscious, killed, or incapacitated.

You may run away by making a ***MERP*** "medium" moving manoeuvre (add your appropriate Moving Manoeuvre Bonus) and getting a result of "100" or more. These results are cumulative from round to round, so you might be able to run away over the course of several rounds (e.g., a result of "60" on the first round and a "50" on the second round would mean that you successfully "*Run Away*" at the end of the second round).

Taking Damage

Often the text will instruct you to *increase your Damage Taken* by a certain amount. Here are some suggested ways for translating that damage into ***MERP*** damage (***Pick a Number*** will be referred to as "2-12"):

QuestGame™ **Damage Taken**	***MERP*** **Damage**
A fixed number	Same number of ***MERP*** concussion hits
(2-12) once	A ***MERP*** "A" Critical Strike + 1-10 hits
(2-12) twice	A ***MERP*** "C" Critical Strike + 1-10 hits
(2-12) 3 times	A ***MERP*** "E" Critical Strike + 1-10 hits
etc.	etc.

The type of "Critical Strike" can be determined by the situation (e.g., for a fall, use "impact" criticals, for fire, use "heat" criticals). When in doubt, use "unbalancing" criticals.

Resistance Rolls

The *QuestGame*™ system uses the *Magical* bonus to resolve situations that would require "Resistance Rolls" (RR's) in ***MERP***. When you encounter these situations, follow the ***MERP*** RR procedure using the bonus appropriate for the situation (e.g., use the Poison RR bonus versus poisons); when in doubt with regards to spells assume that they are Essence spells.

If the RR involves an opponent or a trap, use the levels given in the ***MERP*** Stats Table as the attack level for the RR. Otherwise, use an attack level of 3.

If you fail an RR, follow the instructions indicated by the lowest of the ranges given. If you resist, follow the instructions indicated by the highest of the ranges given.

If three ranges are given and you resist, use the highest range. If three ranges are given and you fail an initial RR, make a second RR. If you fail the second, use the lowest range. If you resist on the second RR, use the middle range.

Magic Items

An item with a +1 bonus in the *QuestGame*™ system should have a +5 bonus in ***MERP*** and vice versa.

WE NEED YOUR FEEDBACK ON

MINES OF MORIA

PLEASE HELP US DO A BETTER JOB ON FUTURE BOOKS BY ANSWERING SOME OR ALL OF THE FOLLOWING QUESTIONS & SENDING YOUR REPLIES TO I.C.E.

I purchased this book at ____________________________
____________________________________(name of store).

I am (male/female)________ and ________years of age. I am in the _________ grade in school.

I live in a (small, medium, large) ______________town/city.

My favorite magazine is ____________________________.

I heard about this gamebook through __________________
____________________ (a friend, family member, an advertisement, other ____________________________).

The one thing I like the *most* about this Middle-earth Quest gamebook is ______________________________________
____.

The one thing I like the *least* about this Middle-earth Quest gamebook is ______________________________________
____.

Send all feedback replies to:

IRON CROWN ENTERPRISES
DEPT. MEQ
P.O. BOX 1605
CHARLOTTESVILLE, VA. 22902

MIDDLE-EARTH ROLE PLAYING™

MIDDLE-EARTH ROLE PLAYING (MERP) is a Fantasy Role Playing Game system perfect for novices as well as experienced gamers! Based on THE HOBBIT and THE LORD OF THE RINGS, MERP provides the structure and framework for role playing in the greatest fantasy setting of all time. . . . J.R.R. Tolkien's Middle-earth! MERP is well supported by a wide variety of game aids, Campaign Modules, Adventure Supplements, and Ready-to-Run Adventures. MIDDLE-EARTH ROLE PLAYING. . . . a world apart!

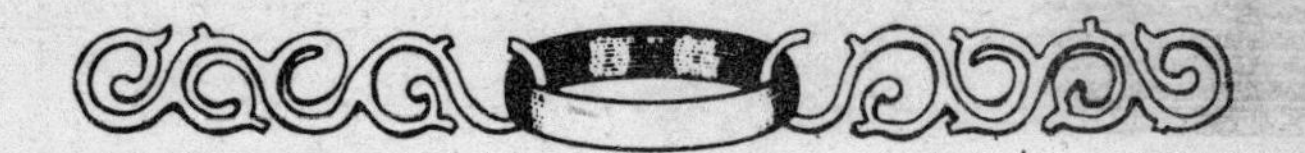

Produced & Distributed by
IRON CROWN
ENTERPRISES INC.
P.O. Box 1605
Charlottesville, VA 22902

MERP STATS TABLE

(See *MERP* Table ST-2 for an explaination of the codes)

Text #	Type (number)	Level	Speed	Hits	AT	DB	Attack	Size	Crit
113	Troll	10	MD	175	Pl	60	150Ba	L	Lge
114	Troll	10	MD	175	Pl	30	150Ba	L	Lge
125	Orc #1	1	MD	20	No	5	30We	M	Reg
	Orc #2	2	MD	35	No	15	45We	M	Reg
	Orc #3	3	MD	45	No	10	55We	M	Reg
127	Cave Bats	1	VF	20	No	80	15Bi	S	Reg
157	Orc #1	5	MD	55	No	15	55We	M	Reg
	Orc #2	1	MD	20	No	0	40We	M	Reg
	Orc #3	2	MF	24	No	20	30Cl	M	Reg
	Orc #4	6	MD	62	SL	15	75We	M	Reg
189	Giant Spider	12	MF	200	RL	25	100St	L	Lge
199	Water Creature	10	MD	80	RL	5	140Cr	L	Lge
203	Orc #1	2	MD	40	No	15	40We	M	Reg
	Orc #2	1	MD	26	No	5	30We	M	Reg
209	Cave Snake	1	MD	20	SL	0	55Cr	M	Reg
220	Use the Stats from 199								
231	Dwarf	5	MD	80	Ch	30	80We	M	Reg
234	Orc #1	3	MD	60	No	10	70We	M	Reg
	Orc #2	2	MD	40	No	5	50We	M	Reg
	Orc #3	1	MD	26	No	0	20We	M	Reg
257	Use the Stats from 125.								
259	Use the Stats from 199.								
412	Use the Stats from 231.								